ANSON B. WALKER

Free to Be the Best Me

How Abuse, Jail and Near-Death Inspired "The Walker Lifestyle" To Help You Become Your Best

Coach [...]

You imp[...] a teenager positively [...] [...] you will eve[r] know sir. Masculine, Christian Male.... Thank you!! Don't change a thing sir!

Anson B. Walker

THE WALKER LIFESTYLE

v/r,

Anson B. Walke[r]

First edition

This book was professionally typeset on Reedsy.
Find out more at reedsy.com

Contents

Foreword   vi

Preface   viii

Acknowledgement   xi

What They're Saying About Anson...   xii

I   Southern Trouble

1   Mississippi Minefields   3

Great Dad, Bad Husband   6

Mom on Tape   8

Bully Beware   9

Sports Therapy   10

6 Keys to Preparing Yourself to Win   15

2   School of Hard Knocks   19

From Broker to Behind Bars   22

The Book   25

3   Navy Days: Private Seaman Walker   26

Bootcamp Brainwashing   27

3 Ways to Increase Your Courage   28

4   The Accident   35

6 Ways to Win in Tough Times   39

Enough's Enough   41

II   Health Reborn

5 Walking The Walker Lifestyle   49
  4 Ways to Living Your Values   58
6 Ground Rules of The Walker Lifestyle   62
  Find Your Motivation   63
  10 Ways People Sabotage Positive Change   65
  Discipline = Freedom   69
  Commit Like a Convict — Be Consistent   70
  Stay Positive   71
  Make Friends, Family with Fitness   72
  Show that You Care   74
  Focus on Fat Loss — Forget about Weight Loss   76
  Lose the Booze   77
  Good Intake = Good Outtake   77
  Pretenders vs. Contenders   82
  Strengthen to Lengthen Life   87
  Cardio: The Great Equalizer   91
  Rest for Recovery   93
  Supplement Success   95
7 Photo Story   96

III Inspiring Freedom

8 Writing the Next Chapter   113
  From Wheelchair to Walking   114
  From Fat to Fit   117
  Answering Prayers   120
  Paralyzed but Not Permanently   122
9 Ready For Love   125
  Letter from Tiffany   128

10 The Best Me   132
    My (Your) 2022 Declarations   134
    What's Next for Me?   139
    Closing Anson-isms   143
11 The Best You   145

Appendix   150
    The 7-Day Reboot Bootcamp   150
    DAY 1 — Chest and Triceps   152
    DAY 2 — Legs and Biceps   156
    DAY 3 — Shoulders   159
    DAY 4 — Back and Triceps   162
    DAY 5 — Wildcard   166
    Defeating Myths about The Walker Lifestyle   167
About the Author   174

Foreword

Dear Reader:

I met Anson the summer before we both attended the same college in 1994. We had a lot in common, and although I was never able to put my finger on "it" back then, we had a unique connection. We became roommates in the dorm, teammates on the baseball field, fraternity brothers, and lifelong friends. Although our paths after college were very different, a high degree of mutual respect for how we have both persevered through difficult challenges in life is the fuel for our continued bond.

I was there for many of his lowest moments, described in this book with brutal honesty. Total honesty with oneself, Anson believes, is owning both success and defeat, a concept he claims today as the single most important hurdle to real emotional healing and true personal growth. We have witnessed some of each other's least proud moments. He watched me chase my dream of practicing medicine, which came with many challenges and early failures of its own. I feel honored to have been asked to provide this "letter to the reader" of sorts for a book that was undoubtedly a very difficult but also therapeutic process, and one whose title exemplifies its author's intent and purpose so well.

Anson and I have maintained a close relationship for nearly thirty years and have had many deep, personal conversations. Therefore, the facts surrounding the experiences that shaped his life do not provide the same shock value to me as they certainly will for others. Nevertheless, he has done a wonderful job of describing the impactful events of his life in an organized, temperate manner. This effectively establishes the credibility needed to provide such advice and inspiration to others, only earned if one "practices what he preaches."

For Anson, living with lies and fearing the truth was destroying him. Always physically strong and athletic, he proved that emotional strength is equally crucial to operating your life at the highest level and being truly healthy. This book is a "call to action" for many of us needing the motivation to accept our faults and inconsistencies rather than deny them. In the end, Anson helps us understand that by disguising or suppressing our past failures and disappointments, we neglect one of the ultimate tools of change in our own lives. He teaches us that a healthy mindset is a product of exercise too, but it cannot be strengthened by the gym alone.

Here's to being your best,

Kirk Kinard, DO
    Owner-Medical Director
    Willow Pain and Wellness, LLC

Preface

The Walker Lifestyle is designed to help you become the best you can be. It's not about comparing yourself to others. It's about being better today than you were yesterday. It's a series of habits. A mindset. Small changes that have big results. Discipline that leads to freedom. Making good choices, even when it's hard, motivates more good choices. It's about taking and maintaining control over the two things you can control: attitude and effort.

God made the body to work. We're not like engines. There are only so many miles on an engine until it wears out. Our bodies are just the opposite. The more we use our bodies, the better they get.

I don't have a secret formula. What I offer is a way of life, a fresh approach, and a realistic perspective based on my experiences learning about the value of life itself. I've learned the hard way that life is a privilege, and our body, mind, and soul are gifts. But health is our responsibility.

In this book, I'm going to reveal how I came to this point. Of course, I'll explain key fitness and nutrition concepts, but the best trainer in the world can't help you if you do not value life or care about the health of your body, mind, and soul. On the other hand, if you do care and commit yourself to improving, you're going to win, and win big.

Regardless of where you're at today, I hope my story will bring a new perspective about life that inspires you to use today for what it is — an opportunity.

I'm going to be 100 percent transparent, 100 percent true to who

I am, and 100 percent holistic. There's no better way to live. I've tasted unthinkable abuse, financial success, utter failure, complete brokenness, and near-death. I've overcome eleven surgeries on my shoulders, elbows, knees, and back. Yet today, at the age of forty-seven, I'm stronger and better than I have ever been.

> **Taking care of your health is not selfish,**
> **it's selfless.**
> **— Anson-ism**

I'm a Southern boy, through and through, born and raised in Mississippi. So I hope y'all don't mind some straight shootin' along the way. I don't take myself too seriously, except when it comes to serving those around me who want The Walker Lifestyle and what it promises. Some of this Southern personality has been coined by clients as "Anson-isms," which I'll pepper throughout. Plus, I'm including some good ol' fashioned wisdom taught by my dad, which I call "The Dan Walker Rules," that I have lived by my whole life.

My intentions are honorable. But I do make mistakes, and I've made some doozies. The key is to own up to them instead of denying them. Learn from the mistakes and do not make those mistakes again. That's how The Walker Lifestyle was born — from learning from my mistakes.

I believe God put me here to show others how to put these principles to work and become healthy, energetic humans destined for greatness. We owe it to ourselves and our loved ones to become the best we can be. So we will take a look at priorities that define or undermine us. I'll be honest about what defines my priorities and describe powerful ways to remain positive with the process. I just don't have time for anything else.

My life, my story, and my experiences have added up for this moment right now. My sincerest hope is that today you will be better than yesterday because you picked up this book and started to light the fire within.

Acknowledgement

I am forever grateful for help and support in my life from:

- George Taylor, who has been my mentor in the fitness business.
- Pat Irby, from whom I learned about "attention to detail."
- My brother, Matthew Ryan Walker, who has always been there for me. When I think of honesty and integrity, my brother Matt comes to mind. We disagree from time to time, but the one thing we do that most other siblings do not do in my opinion is to "Communicate Effectively!!!" We both know where the other one stands, and we both know how fortunate we are to have one another. It just works. Matt is my best friend and I will have his back forever plus.....I love you little brother!
- Tiffany Gunn Walker for supporting the book and backing me 100 percent to do what I do with The Walker Lifestyle. What can I say about my future bride? She's more beautiful on the inside than out . . . and she's friggin' gorgeous. She lets me do my thing at 99 mph . . . then supports me if I wreck. She knows I honor her in all I do, and it works for us. I love you baby!
- My mom, Shirley Marshall, gave me a second chance in life. I am forever thankful and indebted, and I think if you were to ask her if she's proud of me, you would get a resounding "YES!" Mom, thank you and know this.....I love you very much!

What They're Saying About Anson...

"Anson is the most driven person I've ever met. Not only does he talk the talk, he definitely walks the walk. He is deeply committed to helping others achieve their goals in fitness and wellness."

— John Weaver
Associate High School Headmaster, Offensive Coordinator Varsity Football

"Anson is one of the most adventurous, pure-hearted guys that I know. Love that guy."

— Jeremy Sokovich
Oil and Gas Executive

"Anson's dedication is inspiring to all who know him and work with him. It has shown me how to push myself to become a better me!"

— Lisa McNeal
Executive, John Deere

"Anson Walker is a true Southern Gentleman. A few words that come to mind are loyal, strong, passionate, integrity, kind, dedicated, and TEACHER. I am proud that Anson is my friend/brother."

— David Cuevas

"Anson is an open book. He wants folks to learn and grow from his successes and mistakes. But his desire to help others is genuine."

— Jordan Davis
Business Owner

"A scholar and a gentleman, Anson has forged a rare combination of brains and brawn to overcome adversity and achieve success through helping others. His story is one of determination, faith, and perseverance."

— Donald W. Cumbest II, Esq.

"Anson really has a simple but effective plan for you to live your life in a healthy way. His passion for people to live healthy is incredible; it's easy to see why he's been successful."

— Herbert Davis
Head Football Coach, Madison Ridgeland Academy

"I've known Anson for twenty years now. I have watched him persevere and grow as a leader."

— David Landrum
Business Owner

"Meathead muscle man turned softie! Anson has a kind and selfless heart. I never expected my trainer to become one of my dearest friends.

He helps with my mental strength as much as my physical health."
— Beth Hutchinson
Four-year client of Anson

"I met Anson in August of 1997 at Delta State University. I was playing football with his little brother, Matt. I got to know Anson through the fall and winter of that year and felt an instant connection with him. When I was fourteen years old, I lost my brother in a car wreck in the summer of 1991. Looking back, unknown to me at the time, Anson provided that older brother mentorship that I needed badly. We have remained great friends since that time, and we have both been through much adversity since. Throughout my ups and downs, sorrows and joy, Anson has been a constant rock of support for me, my wife, and my kids. I know Anson went through some trials and tribulations himself, and I never questioned that he would come through it stronger and more focused than ever. Regardless of where one finds himself in life, if you have a 'brother' like Anson on your side you'll be alright. My boy Anson is one of the most solid people I know on this earth."
— Hunter Caston
Comptroller, JanTron, and twenty-five-year friend of Anson

"I met Anson at a Rotary Club meeting in Madison, Mississippi. He was the guest speaker, and his topic was about his life story, its challenges and successes, and how he motivates someone to be the best version of themselves. Well, he had me from the beginning as I was in search of a personal trainer. I became a client, and it fast-forwarded to brotherhood. Anson motivates and inspires our men's fitness group on a daily basis both physically and mentally. From a personal standpoint, his positive attitude and his guidance of putting in the hard work to get the results transcends from the gym into life. I'm proud of him for documenting his life story, and I know it will enhance the lives of his readers. Well done, my friend!"

— Reginald D. Rigsby, M.D.
Family medicine physician, Magnolia Medical Clinic in Madison, Mississippi

I

Southern Trouble

1

Mississippi Minefields

The traumas of life, of which I've experienced many, can give us a lot of great excuses to avoid becoming the best we can be. We tell ourselves they are the reasons we sabotage our own progress, underachieve, have a sour disposition, and perhaps escape all the hard feelings with drugs and alcohol. The garbage we've experienced just gets passed around our relationships in different forms. But there always comes a point in time when you have to face facts and say, "It stops with me."

The toxic buildup started early on for me. I was born in Jackson, Mississippi, at Hinds General Hospital in 1974. I don't remember too much from those early years, except riding on my dad's German Shepherd, named Big Boy. I watched cartoons on Saturday mornings like any other little boy at that time. I was happy, loved, and got plenty of attention. I remember going to church with my parents, and water skiing at the age of four.

I do have one memory, however, that haunted me for more than thirty-five years.

My dad was a man's man, a real hard ass. It was always his way or the highway. There was no democracy at home. It was a dictatorship.

He was 5' 11" and thick as a tree trunk. He may have been a little overweight, but he was strong. He didn't exercise, because he developed strength as a welder. He built things. His daddy started the Jackson Casket Company. So my dad grew up lifting caskets, and turned into an intimidating man. He didn't back down from anything. He wore Levi's, T-shirts, and flannels while smoking three packs a day of Vantage Ultra Light cigarettes. He was a hard-working man. His word was his bond. He believed in honor, pride, integrity, and work ethic.

When the weekends came around, my dad would start drinking Miller Light. But he always ended up with Jack Daniel's whiskey. He got loud, aggressive, and dominating, especially with my mom. I remember him hollering at her. I never felt threatened, but it scared me nonetheless.

When I was four years old, my dad took me on a deep-sea fishing trip with a few friends of his and their sons. We loaded up the cars, hitched up two boats, and drove to the shores of the Gulf of Mexico where we rented a mobile home.

We went out to sea on the first day, and I don't remember much except trying to stay out of the way. I did make friends with one of the boys, a ten-year-old I followed around. When we got back, we settled down for dinner. As the evening wore on, this boy brought me into the bathroom.

I figured he thought I was cool and wanted to show me something. Well, I was half right. He definitely wanted to show me something.

"I want you to hold me like this," he said while putting my hand around his junk. It escalated quickly, if you know what I mean.

"If you don't, I'm not going to be your friend," I remember him saying. I really didn't know any better, although I felt weird about this whole thing. But I did want to be friends, so I honored his requests until it was over. He told me to do this and that. Then he did the same things to me. "Now, don't tell your dad. This is our special secret, okay?"

I looked up to him. Although I didn't feel right about it, I kept it a secret.

Unfortunately, we went fishing two or three times a year with the same father and son. Every time, if he could get me alone, we'd play the same routine. Sometimes, on the drive down or driving back, we'd crawl into the camper that was set onto our big Ford extended pickup truck. Just a few feet away from my dad in the cab, it would happen again. I didn't like doing it, but I couldn't do anything about it either.

Finally, after I turned seven, I told him, "Man, I don't like this." Thank God he didn't force me, and it just kind of went away. It never happened again, but it traumatized the hell out of me for many years. You just can't take that out of your brain. It's a vivid memory etched in there forever.

As I grew older, I began feeling ashamed of what had happened. I learned it wasn't right, but I didn't tell anyone. I just had to bury the guilt from it all.

I started second-guessing myself: "Why didn't I say something to my dad? Why didn't I just stop that boy?" It affected my sense of who I was. The way I was raised, that was not normal. So did that mean I was not normal? From then on, I was damaged goods. I bottled up those memories the best I could until adulthood. But whenever I heard about a pedophile or saw sexual abuse in a movie, it brought me back to the camper and fishing trip. The only reason I told anyone about it was because my brother and his wife, Christy, had two girls. When their youngest was three, I told my brother and my dad because I knew I couldn't have that happen to my brother's girls.

Still, in an odd way, this abuse played a role in my development of The Walker Lifestyle. It's given me compassion for others, which allows me to serve them with all I've got.

Great Dad, Bad Husband

When I was five, my brother Matt was born, and my mom took us to live with her parents on their farm thirty miles away in Canton, Mississippi. At the time, I didn't understand why my dad wasn't around. I just figured he was working, and I missed him a bunch. But in fact, my parents were fixing to divorce.

For the next three years, Matt and I saw my dad every other weekend. We missed him, and he missed us.

During this time, I started playing baseball, beginning with T-ball. After that season, I moved into fast-pitch baseball. In my first season as a seven-year-old, I don't think I got one hit the whole year. The next time my dad visited, I told him. "Dad, the coach's son made the all-star team and I didn't. I don't think it's fair that he gets to play and I don't. So will you call the coach and tell him it's wrong and that I should be able to play too?"

He looked at me, about to give me the first of many of what I call The Dan Walker Rules. "Son, the reason you didn't make all-stars is because you suck. Now, you can do one of two things. You can pout and complain about it like you're doing right now, or we can start practicing. If you practice hard enough, you can make the all-star team next year. We can start today, but the choice is yours."

I had a decision to make. I said, "Well, I want to start practicing." We did. With every visit, we would break out the bat and balls, and he would throw pitches at me. He would later teach me to play football and basketball. For Christmas that year, I got a concrete slab. Sounds funny, but he put it in our backyard so we could play basketball, baseball and football. Next, he installed outdoor lighting so we could play into the night. From that time on, there was never a sport or season that I didn't make the all-star team. I give my dad the credit.

Besides all the yelling at my mom, I always thought my dad was the best man on the planet. So I was tickled when my mom decided to give him another chance. They remarried three years after the divorce, when I was eight years old.

I may never know all the reasons why she took him back, but I know it helped her financially. Unfortunately, he brought back his weekend habits, which only got worse over time. From the ages of nine to twelve years old, I saw the pattern with a little better understanding. Dad would get drunk and yell at my mom for some unknown reason, and then he would shake her in a rage. He started to scare me too. I knew something wasn't right. Mom seemed to recoil back from life. She lost her personality. She stopped caring about her own health. She was getting beat up without a punch ever being thrown. She was injured mentally and psychologically from the verbal lashings, and she was losing touch as a mother.

When I was twelve, I knew she'd had enough. One Saturday afternoon, my dad pulled Matt and me together for a little talk.

"Y'all are going to live with me because mom and I are . . ." the excuses came out, but I knew what was going on. "Look, tomorrow after church, we're going to have a family talk. Just tell your mom you want to live with me, and that's what we'll do." That's what we did, and my parents divorced again.

That was a sad day for us. I know it cut my mom's heart deeply. From that time until I was eighteen years old, I only saw my mom once a year for Christmas, even though she lived in the same town. My dad was in control now. He was the best Dad I could have ever asked for, but he was a terrible husband.

Mom on Tape

Later on, when I was about twenty-three years old, I learned something else that broke my heart and drove me to renew a relationship with my mom regardless of what my dad said.

My brother, a senior in high school at the time, called me.

"Anson, you're not going to believe what I found," he said.

"What's that?"

"Dad set the home phone to ignore all phone calls, sending all the messages right to the recorder. I found the tape recordings, and guess who has been calling all these years? Mom."

Hearing this felt like taking a sucker punch to the gut. Since I was twelve years old, my dad had been screening all her calls and giving Matt and me a watered-down version.

The truth is, our mom was calling to say, "Hey, son. I love you. When do you want to come see me?" But my dad was intent on ruining our relationship, and in the process, penalizing her for divorcing him the second time. He was out for vengeance, and it cost me many years of knowing and loving my mom.

That's when I started reconnecting with her, and we began by meeting once a month just to visit or have lunch. We had a lot to catch up on, and we made the most of it.

It took time for me to forgive my dad for what he did. But eventually, I had to let that hurt go and focus on becoming the best me — and that included honoring both my mom and my dad the best I could. Forgiveness was not easy, but it was required.

Bully Beware

Between the abuse I experienced personally, my dad's tough love, and watching my mom shrink, I was always looking out for my brother, Matt. No matter where we lived, we always had each other's back. I cared for him and wanted to protect him the best I could.

When I was in seventh grade, my brother was in second grade, and we both went to Canton Academy. One afternoon we were heading home in the carpool after school with five other kids, and I noticed something was wrong with Matt. He wasn't saying a word and was looking out the window lost in his thoughts. I knew that look because I had felt that way when I was that age.

When we got home, I asked him, "What's wrong with you?"

"There's a fourth-grade kid picking on me," Matt said. At that age, two years difference is a big deal.

"What the hell for?" I asked.

"I don't know why. He's just a big bully."

> **Worrying does not take away tomorrow's troubles.**
> **It takes away today's peace.**
> **— Anson-ism**

"Okay, I'll take care of this. Don't you worry," I assured him.

I hatched a plan that started with forging two notes — one for my teacher and one for Matt's. I wrote, "Anson is dismissed at 2:45 instead of 3:00." For Matt's teacher, I wrote the same thing only using Matt's name. I signed off on both of them using my best version of my dad's signature. (This newfound skill to forge signatures would get me into trouble later on, but I'll save that story for another chapter.)

The next day, Matt and I were let out at 2:45, and we headed outside the fourth-grade classroom waiting for the 3:00 bell.

"When he comes out, show me who he is," I told Matt.

"That's him," Matt pointed at the bully, named Joey, who walked out of school unaware of what was going to happen.

Within seconds, I grabbed Joey and threw him up against a wall. I got right into his face.

With my two fists clenched around his collar, I growled at him, "Dude, if you ever mess with him again, I'll kick your ass. You know who that is?"

He nodded and said, "That's Matt."

"That's right, that's Matt Walker, and he's my little brother. Now GIT."

Joey never touched Matt again. Better yet, my brother started walking with his chest puffed up. He was proud of me; he felt safe and had his mojo back.

That's the first time I started fighting for other people's health.

Sports Therapy

I attribute sports for much of what The Walker Lifestyle is all about. Sports require much more than talent or athletic ability. Sports are a metaphor for life. For starters, there are individuals who join together to make a team who compete against an opponent. It's just like in life in that we don't go alone, and we face adversity every day.

Football is a great example. You sacrifice your summers to workouts. You invest your efforts with fifty other people with the same common goal — win on Friday or Saturday. Most people don't realize how much preparation goes into playing football. It takes more than keeping yourself in shape and being ready. I'm talking about reviewing film, learning the playbook, executing as a unit, practicing, game day preparation, being a good teammate or leader, and much more. When that all comes together, it's an unbelievable feeling.

The purpose is to win, but there is something to learn no matter whether you win or lose. Improving yourself and the team doesn't end if you have a higher number on the scoreboard. Losses bring another challenge — resiliency and a never-give-up attitude. Losing hurts more than winning feels good, but both play a role in developing yourself for life.

Besides hunting and fishing, if there was a ball around, I would be playing with it. I grew up with sports, and sports grew me up — on and off the field. I started playing organized sports with baseball when I was eight years old. My dad never made me do it, but when I did join a team, he had a few rules I call "The Dan Walker Rules."

One of my dad's rules was: "Never quit once you've started the season." He would explain that quitting hurts yourself, the coach, and the other teammates. There were times I wanted to throw in the towel, because at the time it was easier than trying to hit a fastball. I didn't quite understand the reason for the rule back then, but I do now. Quitting during the season is a loser move. I've seen others do it, and it just shows a lack of character and lets everyone down.

Sports came naturally for me, while schoolwork tended to take a back seat in my mind. By my dad's standards, that didn't measure up. So my brother and I learned the next Dan Walker Rule: "If you make a C, you don't play. Grades come first." That was not a school rule, that was my dad's.

I remember him saying, "I don't give a shit about sports. I care about your grades."

When I was in ninth grade, I made a C on an algebra test. So my dad made me sit out for two basketball games until I made an A on my next test.

I had to tell the coach, "Coach I'm benched. I made a C."

"Well, you're still eligible," he said.

"Not with Dan Walker I'm not. I've got to sit." So I benched myself, wearing slacks and a nice shirt during the games. I didn't like the view from the bench for the next two games, and I couldn't wait for the next algebra test.

Finally, it did come. I was ready and scored 100 percent on the test, raising my overall grade to a B. I never had a C again the rest of my life.

I played football, basketball, baseball, and track every year until I graduated from Canton Academy High School. From there, I played football and baseball in college. I started at Holmes Junior College in Goodman, Mississippi, and then moved on to Millsaps College in Jackson, Mississippi, where I graduated with a Bachelor's Degree in Business Administration. At Millsaps I played football and baseball, earning All-Conference honors in both. I just always excelled at it, but I learned to work hard too.

Back when I was a junior in high school, about sixteen years old, I had a coach, Bill Buckley. He taught me, "People may be more talented than you, but you can control whether you work harder than them. Hard work beats talent when talent doesn't work."

So I knew if I always worked harder than everybody else, I could control whether I played, whether I started, and to a certain degree, how good I became. So my motto was "nobody outworks me." I had talent, but nobody outworked me.

I was a pitcher in baseball. I had four good pitches — a fastball, slider, curve, and change-up — and nine locations to aim at over the plate. When I was on, it was game over for the other side. But there were many times I was not at my best. But I still competed as best I could.

It's the same thing with The Walker Lifestyle. When I show up to the gym at 4:30 a.m., I don't always have my A game every day. But I still show up and do my best. I still get that workout in. When I'm done,

I feel great. I can assure you, in the thousands of workouts I've done, I've never regretted one in my whole life.

With sports, competition drives the game. But with The Walker Lifestyle, the competition is me — or you. Instead of winning the game on Friday night, we're trying to win today. To be better today than we were yesterday, that's the goal. That's how you win in life.

> *To be better today than we were yesterday,*
> *that's the goal. That's how you win in life.*
> *— Anson ïsm*

Sports develop a respect for sacrifice, hard work, and loyalty. You learn about roles, relationships, and overcoming adversity. These are principles baked into The Walker Lifestyle. If you live by these principles, you'll win in fitness and in life.

Sports also teach sportsmanship — which is a way of behaving that includes gratitude for the privilege, playing by the rules, and being honest and humble. This is a big deal, particularly as it applies to The Walker Lifestyle. Let me explain.

I think you can win graciously, and you can lose graciously. You can win like a jerk, and you can lose like a jerk. I believe that. I saw this many times in my career, but one moment stands out. In my junior year in college, we played in Danville, Kentucky, against a team who had a first baseman who was the reigning player of the year. He was a bad-ass, about 6'3", 235 pounds. From the pitcher's mound, I watched him settle into the batter's box, crowding the plate. So I wanted to back him off with a few 90 mph high-and-tight fastballs, then get him swinging at my curve balls going away from him.

Unfortunately, my fastball got away from me a bit and hit him in the forearm. I could hear it crack on impact.

In an instant, his senior-year season was over.

After the game, I walked into his dugout, and he was sitting there with ice on his arm.

"Hey big fella," I said. "I'm so damn sorry about that. You're so good. I was trying to back your big ass off the plate so I could bring that slider, or that curve ball, and get you on your heels to keep you from knocking it out on me."

He looked at me, and said, "Walker, that's baseball. It happens, brother. Don't worry about it."

I'll never forget that lesson from that player. He handled it with true sportsmanship instead of being all pissed off at me. He took the high road.

I learned that life happens, good and bad, and regardless of what happens, I need to keep an attitude like that player who was able to forgive easily and focus on what's ahead.

That is just one example of how sports played a big part in my development as an individual. But if I had to boil down everything I learned into one word, it would be *consistency*.

Consistency wins every time. If you're consistent with your workouts and mindset, then you will win. Consistency brings out the best in us, win or lose. Even if I'm injured, consistency is called for. Injuries are not excuses to lay off your goals. There are some injuries that are worse than others, but if I can stand up, I'll stay consistent and play hurt.

Consistency is my secret weapon, and playing hurt is an example. I'm not talking about serious injuries. But here's an example: When I had knee replacement surgery on a Thursday, I was training clients on crutches the following Monday. People can't help but respect that.

----

6 Keys to Preparing Yourself to Win

Winning in life doesn't just happen by chance or coincidence. I believe the first step you take in winning is being prepared for tough times. Because, guess what, tough times are literally right around the corner. You have to be prepared to lead your loved ones through adversity. You accomplish this by leading yourself first.

Knowing yourself, and knowing how you win, is how you prepare to win. You have to know what's best and effective for you and your family at any time!

In difficult times, you have to remain true to your values, no matter what. I have a few things going for me, and the most important thing is I'll never break for anyone is my word, my integrity, or my values. Period!

In preparing to win in life, you can't get to where you want to go until you know exactly where you are! How do you determine where you are? You have to work at self-awareness. Winners examine and understand their temperament. They know exactly what personal experiences have served them well. They know their energy levels, their daily, monthly, and seasonal rhythms. Winners know which kinds of people they work well with and which kinds they have to try harder to appreciate. Winners have a sense of where they want to go and how they can get there.

Knowing yourself on a deep level isn't quick or easy. It is a long and involved process. Some of it isn't particularly fun. I know this firsthand. But it is necessary if you want to win in the gym, in business, in your family, or in the classroom! Self-knowledge is critical to winning in life. I believe that 100 percent.

Here are six keys that will prepare you to win.

1. **Determine What You Stand For** — *This is the heart of your character.*

Your personal values are the criteria you use to drive your behavior. We all must determine what we will live for, stand for, and die for — or else someone else will do it for us. As a winner, the values you embrace and model will also determine who follows you and why!

2. ***Be a Servant Leader*** *— Serving others is the highest level of achievement on God's green earth in my opinion. I honestly believe the only worthy motivation for leadership or a leadership position is a desire to serve others. So-called leaders or managers who do not put people, family first ultimately disqualify themselves as leaders. Why? Because people don't care how much you know until they know that you care. Period.*

3. ***Discover Your Purpose*** *— Be sure you understand the reason why you do something. You can't grow to your potential if you don't know and fully comprehend your purpose. And if you don't know why you're on this earth and you are not able to improve in that purpose to the best of your ability, you'll be very limited in the ways you can help others. Once you understand your purpose, you need to prioritize your life to that purpose. If you don't, you'll continually get off track and you may never feel a real sense of fulfillment and completion. The reason I know this to be true is because I've experienced unfulfillment, drifting in life. Just going through the motions is an empty feeling. I'll never, ever go back to that.*

4. ***Live with Integrity*** *— Live with integrity before attempting to lead others. In the history of successful teams and businesses, the winning teams are made up of people with diverse skills. But when it comes to values, habits, discipline, and attitudes, there has to be unity. When it comes to my clients and The Walker Lifestyle, I have to set the example. Discipline has to be a top priority. Undisciplined leaders do sloppy work, waste people's time, and usually treat people poorly. At least that's been my experience. If you constantly do more than you expect from others, others will respect you, and the chances are good they will follow you.*

That goes for your subordinates at work, co-workers, your family at home, and clients. It works, trust me.

5. **Build Relationships** — *I made a conscious effort years ago to introduce myself to new gym members. That has improved my quality of life. Now gym members who are not even clients tell me about their families, personal stuff, and ask me questions periodically. I love our gym members. If you want to win more in life, become highly relational.*

6. **Rededicate Yourself to Growth and Self-Discipline** — *Winners must keep growing in order to keep winning! Winning doesn't just happen. What are you reading right now that will help you win in life? Winners must keep growing, keep learning in order to keep winning. You can't expect your people, your family to grow and improve if you don't. This is especially important during tough times, because tough times bring change. The only way to adapt to change is to grow. Tough times demand that you do!*

Friends, joining a gym is about self-improvement. It's about competing with yourself daily. It's about taking ownership of yourself. Taking accountability and responsibility for your immune system and your physical and mental health. Who else is going to do it? Your doctor? Your pharmacist? Probably not. Medical professionals can give you advice, but they can't force you to get enough exercise, sunlight, sleep, and vitamins. You have to make those choices yourself. Take responsibility for yourself, join a gym, and try The Walker Lifestyle. It has the power to change you forever.

In other words, stay consistent even if you don't feel like it.

Anybody can "be consistent" when they feel like it. What separates the winners from the losers is that the winners do it when they don't feel like it. Losers skip or quit.

I don't think it'll ever change. How many times do you actually *want* to go hit the gym? Most times, I don't feel like it, and excuses run through my brain. I'm tired. My ass is dragging. I only got four hours of sleep. But when you make yourself work out, once you're done, you've accomplished something whether or not you brought your A game.

Sports carried me through a lot of hard times growing up. They gave me a dream to shoot for — to play professionally — and they gave me an education. But on top of all that, they taught me about the intangibles necessary for life, and The Walker Lifestyle. Like I've said, The Walker Lifestyle is a mindset more than anything else. You don't have to be a competitive athlete to learn about the values of hard work, sacrifice, never quitting, loyalty, how to be gracious, knowing your roles in life, overcoming adversity, and playing hurt. But if you do learn these, you're going to win.

2

School of Hard Knocks

After graduating from college, I received an invitation letter to try out at an upcoming NFL combine. I held the letter and dream in my hands, and suddenly I realized it wasn't my dream anymore. "There's more to life," I thought. I received another letter, this one from Delta State University in Cleveland, Mississippi, to assist in the Athletic Department. My brother, Matt, was attending Delta State and playing on the football team. So I decided that summer that I would forget about the NFL and go to Delta State where I could work in the Athletic Department while earning a Master's in Business Administration.

By then, staying in shape was just a natural part of my lifestyle. So it was great being able to work out with the athletes, and watch Matt's development from the sideline. Time flew by, and soon enough I had an MBA and was ready to earn some money.

A friend referred me to CitiGroup, which is a financial investment firm. I remember going up there for the interview and noticing the parking lot full of Land Rovers, Mercedes-Benzes, and Beemers. Everyone wore suits and ties, looking real sharp. The money trap was set, and I accepted the job as an investment broker. Simple as that.

First, I had to pass exams in life insurance, health insurance, and securities, and then I had to become a licensed mortgage broker. After that I started selling, basically calling people asking if they'd let me invest all their money. I was good at selling, always have been. And the money started rolling in.

For the first time in my life, I was making more money than I knew what to do with. I didn't grow up with this kind of cash around, so it was like being a kid in the candy shop with an open wallet.

An eventual business partner and friend at the time owned a house on a golf course in Annandale, which is a premier neighborhood near Madison, Mississippi. I moved in. By the time I turned twenty-seven years old, I had more money than I'd ever seen. You'd think I would have been smart and invested that money or saved some for a rainy day. But I didn't. Instead, we took limos everywhere, partied hard, and chased women on a daily basis. Money was flying out the window while I was having a good time. My head, unfortunately, was also getting too big for my shoulders.

About three years into this job, I noticed a loophole in the system that I could easily take advantage of. The problem is that it wasn't really a *legal* loophole.

My job was to get a good return on investment for my clients. So I'd sell a term policy and use a piece of that cash value to invest in a high-end mutual fund or high-end stock. Every month you get to see how you're doing. When I got a statement making 8, 10, 12, 20 percent on the money, I felt like I was walking on water. The clients were happy with 6 percent return, so I got the idea that I could continue delivering 6 percent returns, while skimming off the rest into my own pocket. All it took was for me to forge their signatures, and I would start getting checks mailed to my house.

Technically, it was embezzling. But to me at the time, it was business. As long as the clients were happy, I was happy too.

One night, my roommate told me about his father being killed in an off-shore rig accident, leaving him millions of dollars. I offered to put that money to work and began the same routine behind my partner's back. After forging about fifteen checks, literally stealing from my buddy, he finally caught wind of my action. He confronted me and gave me six months to return the money or else he would file charges.

That was a lot of money, a couple hundred thousand, so I had to up my skimming routine. But it caught up with me. My boss finally saw discrepancies in the accounts I was managing. I couldn't explain it away, so they fired me and had all my licenses revoked. There I was, in a rainstorm of my own making.

Near the end of 2003, the market took a huge dip, and I had put an option on my friend's inheritance money, which means I — or we — lost a lot of money. With all the extra skimming, I was able to pay back all but $76,000. But with the market dip, I couldn't come up with the money, and my friend lost his patience and filed charges.

A high school buddy from the Madison County Sheriff's Department called me.

"Anson, what the hell have you done? There's a warrant out for your arrest."

Reality started to set in. "Oh shit." But I was no fool, I wasn't going to run away from this. It's a small town, and I didn't want to be cuffed and stuffed into the back seat of a cop car. So I asked my dad to drop me off at the station.

"What for?" he asked.

"It's just some bullshit. Don't worry about it." I hated lying to him, but I hated the truth even more.

I just want to make this real clear. What I was doing was disgusting. It's downright dishonorable. It's wrong. It's lying. It's stealing. It's cheating. When I got the dumb idea, it felt weird the first two or three times. But by the fifth time, it became easy. I had justified my behavior

21

because everyone was making money. Everybody's winning, right?

That's how I added things. Maybe I got addicted to that particular game. But that's not who I am. Believe it or not, I thank God I got caught. Because I can tell you that I was on a path to destruction with that lifestyle.

From Broker to Behind Bars

I turned myself in and sat in the holding cell in my street clothes for two days. During this time, my family was deciding what to do with me. My dad was disgusted and basically disowned me right then. My mom didn't know what to do. So I started to face the reality that I was in jail, with no plans to get out anytime soon.

After two days, an officer finally told me to get a shower and put on the orange jumpsuit — inmate No. 18899. They gave me a bag of extra clothes and put me into the general population. That's when it got really scary. I was shaking. It didn't take long to notice that I was the only white boy there, at least in my pod. There were ten pods with thirty-two people each. In my pod, there were thirty-one African-Americans and me.

My roommate was a fifty-seven-year-old, black guy named Bruce. I remember the stark contrast of his gray beard on his skin. He was in for murder, which he said was done in self-defense. But the judge called it manslaughter. I didn't sleep a wink that first night in the top bunk. I just sat there, thinking to myself while listening to Bruce's heavy breathing, "What have you done? Your life is over. I can't believe this is real."

I kept my mouth shut in fear for three days. But daily we were let out in the yard for fresh air and exercise. There was a basketball court where I watched some heated battles play out. Finally, I got the gumption to try to get into the game in order to get my mind off the reality. After all, I was 6'2", and I could hoop.

That first time, I was the last guy picked. But things changed after that. We won, and won again. Pretty soon, they started calling me "Bird," earning some credibility with the fellas, which I'm pretty sure saved my life.

I started accepting the fact that this was my life now. It was a new reality that I had to adapt to or get my ass whooped.

Fear does not stop death. It stops life.
— *Anson-ism*

Besides daily hoops, the only thing to do in jail is eat, sleep, read, do some push-ups and sit-ups, and play cards.

I grew up playing cards, particularly Spades. That's what country folks do, just like the black folks. One night, I was playing Spades in the general population area. We played on a metal table, sitting on metal chairs, and I was about three hands in. Then this black dude, about 6'1", 200 pounds came up to me and put his chest right into my shoulders.

"I had downs, honky," he said to me, which means he was telling me that I stepped into the game even though he was next. It wasn't true, but he wanted to intimidate me into quitting.

I didn't say anything.

"Hey, mother f_____, I see you. You hear me cracker? I had downs," he said louder.

"Obviously you didn't because I'm playing. We're three hands in. You get the next hand," I told him, trying to calm things down.

But he kept pushing himself on me, almost pushing me out of my

23

seat. My mind was racing because I knew how dangerous things could get. But I stood up suddenly and threw a punch that landed on his jaw. With my left hand, I shoved his chest and knocked him right on his ear. I got on top of him, and grabbed him by the throat.

"I'll f—-ing kill you mother f____r" I yelled in his face.

The place went silent. Everyone just looked at me. I sat back down, and we kept playing cards, although I was shaking.

That night, I didn't sleep a wink. I was pretty sure I would get shanked. For the next two days, my head was on a swivel looking around for an imminent attack that never came. I must have passed the test. Or God protected me. Either way, they left this white boy alone after that.

Most of the days were spent in our cells. Every other day, someone would push a cart full of books around to each cell. I'd always grab four or five at a time. I was reading at least a book a day, usually at a little table we had, and using the light from the bathroom that allowed me to read, often until 3:00 a.m. I didn't spend a lot of time with the general population or watch TV. I just read. If I wasn't sleeping or eating, I was reading. It helped pass the time. Plus, it kept my mind occupied; otherwise it was plain depressing to think about what had become of my life.

By the eleventh or twelfth day, all the Anson Walker self-assurance was gone. I was in that orange jumpsuit and not going anywhere. The guilt and shame really started eating away at me. I was embarrassed and felt I had embarrassed my whole family. I can't even describe to you how bad the guilt was. It was a lot to handle, especially imagining how I was living the high life just a few weeks earlier. I went from the penthouse to the jailhouse.

The Book

I was raised in the church, with parents and grandparents who identified as Christian. But my own faith in God took a back seat to sports, girls, and my money-scheming lifestyle. There's no doubt I was going Anson's way instead of God's way.

On my fifteenth day in jail, a book title seemed to jump off the cart to get my attention. It was *Rebel with a Cause*, by Franklin Graham. I knew that name, the son of Rev. Billy Graham, rest his soul. Once I opened that book, I couldn't put it down. I related to Franklin's story because he talked about finding God early on because he didn't want to embarrass his father. But he didn't follow God wholeheartedly. When he was around twelve years old, he would sneak outside his bedroom window and smoke cigarettes. Behind his Daddy's back, he had a rebellious lifestyle until he was twenty years old or so.

I can't remember the whole story now, but he finally came to a point where he realized God was real. And God took it from there, entering into his heart. Franklin wrote about how he was changing his ways because he had a new sense that God was with him.

You could say the same thing happened to me after reading that book. I felt like a rebel with a cause too, and realized it wasn't too late to change. I asked God to forgive me. Then I pleaded with him, "God, if you'll give me a second chance, I promise to honor you. I'll make you proud. Please God, please."

From then on, I prayed and read the Bible every day. I felt God in my life and started living for Christ. I felt hope again, and I thought if I was lucky I could get out of jail someday and live in a halfway house, and be totally happy with that. I knew I would have a felony on my record, so job options would be few and far between. But God wasn't finished with Anson Walker.

3

Navy Days: Private Seaman Walker

During this time in jail, my parents — who hadn't spoken to each other in more than twenty years — were trying to figure out what they could do for me. My mom decided she could sell some property she owned and repay my debt of $76,000. That would also give me another day in court to reassess my penalty, and maybe get me out of jail.

After thirty-one days in jail, I had another day in court to face the judge. When he walked into that courtroom, I was nearly floored over. He had been my fifth grade basketball coach!

During the sentencing, he gave me an offer. "Son, I believe you would benefit from structure and discipline in your life. If your debt is indeed paid back, I'll drop all the charges if you join the U.S. Navy."

"Judge," I started to plead with him like I had pleaded with God. "I've embarrassed myself. I've embarrassed my family long enough. If you're serious about this, I'll go into the Navy, and I promise you, I'll make you proud of your decision."

We struck a deal, and my life was about to take another big-time pivot. After getting my stuff from jail, I couldn't thank my mom enough for giving me the opportunity.

"Mom, I am so grateful and so sorry for what I've put you through," I said. "I promise you that I've changed and will not let you down ever again."

Walking out of that courtroom a free man was a miracle. I knew it cost my mom, and took the mercy of the court, but I know God was pulling all the strings. There's no other explanation. Despite all the cheating, stealing, lying, and disappointing my family and myself, I had received a second chance!

I looked into the blue sky that day, breathed in the fresh air, and found a new appreciation for life. As long as I have breath in these lungs, I knew from that day on that I was different, humble, and grateful. I wanted to find a way to make an honest living, love others as I have been loved, and become the best version of me possible.

Bootcamp Brainwashing

Going into the armed forces like the U.S. Navy was never on my radar. But I decided to jump in with both feet and serve my country the best I could. Still, I'd be lying if I said I wasn't scared about this new twist in my life.

My journey began at the Met station in downtown Jackson, Mississippi. I joined three other new recruits in a van that took us to Jackson International Airport. We flew to Memphis, then to Chicago, where we took another van for a forty-five-minute ride north to Great Lakes, Illinois. That's where we hooked up with about 500 other recruits. Still in civilian clothes, they kept us there for two days where the brainwashing began.

For those two days, we had to stay awake for a series of questions about our life, past, and dirty secrets — a mental mind warping. They tested our will power as we got to the point that we'd tell them anything in order for them to stop screaming at us. It was designed so that we followed orders no matter who we were or where we came from.

----

3 Ways to Increase Your Courage

Friends, let's face it — it can be difficult and risky to win effectively, particularly when times are tough. Courage is necessary. With courage, winners can take risks and go first when they need to. It helps them tackle big problems and face the possibility of failure.

Insecurity can be a major problem in times like today! Insecure managers and workers continually sabotage themselves and others. They worry about their position and standing. They are hesitant to take necessary risks. Insecure folks have a hard time investing in others for fear someone will take their place. I hear this secondhand on a monthly basis. For this reason, among others, people who don't deal with their insecurities and develop courage rarely reach their full potential, and instead of winning they start to lose.

Here are three factors that can help us increase our courage:

1. *Ego — Lose It. The best leaders I know, who are honest with themselves, know that they don't have all the answers. I'm talking to myself loudly! They recognize winning always comes from the combined contributions of everyone on the team. They don't try to answer every question themselves; they don't try to make every decision. You see, winning is a collaborative effort. Let me ask you this: When is the last time someone told you something and you actually listened, actually deeply processed their information and tried to just listen without a reply? The reason I*

ask this is because I used to not listen. I wanted to talk, talk, talk, so people would know how smart I was about my take on this, that, and the other. Guess what, friends, when I started to listen to people about twelve years ago, my knowledge grew to another level. One simple change — shut your doggone mouth and listen! Sounds simple, right? But most can't do it. Why? Ego. Confident winners experience genuine joy in the success of others. When your people win, so do you! So lose your ego.

2. *Give Up the Illusion of Control. Insecure workers try to avoid making mistakes by doing as little as possible or trying to keep a low profile. Insecure managers try to deal with the issue differently. They rely on control. They think if they micromanage people they can keep them from making mistakes. Unfortunately it doesn't work that way. Controlling managers don't understand that progress comes only from taking risks and making mistakes; confident managers and bosses forge ahead, breaking new ground, and occasionally making mistakes. They expect the same from their people. This is going to sound crazy, but I actually like it when I make mistakes. It teaches me what not to do. And I make fun of myself whenever I make a mistake, and we all get a big laugh. It makes you look human! Since you and I can't prevent mistakes, why not adopt an attitude in which you and your team, workers, students, players, and clients learn from the mistakes. Learning from a mistake is called winning!*

3. *Don't Take Trust for Granted. Over the years I've figured out a thing or two or three. Different people view trust in different ways. Secure people see trust as the glue that keeps relationships together and makes business work. Insecure people don't place their trust in others, nor do they invest time, interest, or love into others. As a result, they don't earn trust from others. We should never take trust for granted. By increasing your courage, you will be able to give trust and get it in return. Trust is an honor, and it is earned daily. Think about that! You see, my clients*

trust me. *My friends trust me. My fiancé trusts me. And that trust is earned every day. You know why? Because your daily actions matter. Actions speak louder than words.*

These same three principles apply to The Walker Lifestyle. Ego, control, and trust apply to me and my clients or potential clients. I decided to put my ego on the shelf many years ago. It has made all the difference in my life. It also takes courage, guts to hire a complete stranger to train you. You have to put your ego aside and realize you need help. That's a big deal.

Control is defined as the power to influence or direct people's behavior. I attempt to use control as the power to influence. I know how I feel daily. I know how many hours I'm on my feet every day. I feel fantastic. I want other people to experience that. The Walker Lifestyle is a way of life. Is it the only way? Absolutely not. But it works for me, and it works for my clients. I want you to have a taste of that. From a new client's perspective, it's about relinquishing total control of yourself, listening and applying someone else's philosophy. That's not easy. It takes courage.

Trust is defined as a firm belief in the reliability, truth, and ability or strength of someone or something. Trust is a big factor when it comes to The Walker Lifestyle. I trust my instinct, my knowledge, my creativity, and my work ethic when I'm working with a new person for the first time. There is no standard operation or procedure for training. Each person is unique and complicated. My job is to figure out what will work for you. I take that responsibility seriously. Flipping the script, it takes courage on your part to trust me. It's a big deal, and I know that. I take that commitment very seriously.

Is changing your lifestyle easy? No. Are the results worth it? Yes. If whatever you're doing isn't working, take courage for a ride and change for the better.

Finally, we were assigned to our platoons for bootc; our heads and started teaching us about marching ar history. It was not fun. One day early on, I was ma sure if I was dreaming a nightmare because I was I checked myself and could tell I was up and moving, but it was so surreal.

By the fourth or fifth week, I started grasping the situation mentally and physically. I was named the Master of Arms, in charge of discipline for the platoon — mainly because I was bigger than most of the others. Soon, I started to realize I was going to graduate from bootcamp, and I was going to have a life — eventually. It was certainly better than being in jail.

After bootcamp and about one year of A School (Accession Training), they gave me a dream sheet to list my top three locations of where I'd like to serve. I selected the West Coast first, then East Coast, and then Japan. I was happy when they gave me the West Coast. Southern California, here I come.

Before I left, I went home to say goodbye to my parents. Then I loaded my Yukon truck and drove three days from Mississippi to Oceanside, California, to Camp Pendleton.

I showed up for my assignment in the Naval Hospital. Standing in front of the officer in charge, I said with my Southern twang, "Seaman Walker reporting for duty, sir."

I sat down while the paper shuffling took place. Then behind me I heard someone pop his head into the room.

Smacking his lips, a big black man came in and said, "Shit, dog, where you from?"

"Canton (Can-TAWN), Mississippi. But you might pronounce it Can-ton."

"Shit, I thought I heard something familiar," referring to the sound of my Southern twang.

,√here you from?" I asked.

"I'm from Memphis." That's how I met Samuel Conrad, who became my best friend for the next two years, and whom I still consider "a brother from another mother."

Samuel and I developed a special relationship right from the start. We just clicked. He always says I look like the wrestler Ric Flair. We both served at the Naval Hospital in the same Department of Finance Administration. When we weren't working together, we were hanging out with each other. He took me under his wing and introduced me to the intramural football team. I became the quarterback and captain of the offense, and Samuel played middle linebacker and was captain for the defense. Out of thirty-four teams, we won the championship two years in a row.

After three months or so at Camp Pendleton, I was deployed to serve on the floating hospital ship called the USNS Mercy. We did humanitarian missions, including serving the sick and wounded from the 2004 tsunami that killed 250,000 people in Indonesia, the Philippines, and Malaysia.

My eyes were opened to the poverty in this world. Talk about poor. People in the Mississippi Delta complain of being poor, but we're rich compared to those Third World countries. I've never seen anything like that in my life. The malnutrition was awful.

One day, I wheeled a thirteen-year-old girl onto the ship. She looked pregnant, and she needed attention or she and the baby would not make it. A few days later, I came to check on her as they were wheeling her out. But there was no baby.

"Hey, where's the baby?" I asked the doctors.

"What are you talking about?"

"The baby, with that girl?"

"Oh, she wasn't pregnant. She had a twenty-one-pound tumor inside her stomach, but we removed it."

But that was only one of many examples. Everyone we treated seemed to be under five feet tall and less than 100 pounds. There were many times I just couldn't stop staring at these people because most had never seen a doctor and seemed to be withering away.

Those days on the Mercy Ship made me realize just how damn lucky I am. I don't have problems compared to those folks. They were born into poverty and were likely going to stay in poverty. They don't have a fighting chance, let alone a second chance like I had.

Talk about changing my attitude and my outlook on life. That's when that positivity button came on in Anson Walker's world forever. After that, I started to see that we don't have problems. In the overall scheme of things, we just don't.

When onshore, we had collateral duties. One of my roles was as a Limited Duty Officer, and that's when my fitness training career started coming into focus. My role was to help those who were put on limited duty due to injury or mental or physical limitations. Everyone on limited duty had six months to prepare for their physical tests. If they didn't pass, they were given another six months. After the second try, they had one more chance to pass their physical or they would be separated from service.

We ran, did push-ups and sit-ups and other strength and endurance training. It made me feel good when they were able to pass their tests and return to service. There was no extra compensation, except seeing them make progress in life, which was rewarding enough. I felt like I was changing somebody's life forever. That's when I started thinking that maybe I could make a living helping people get the most from their lives!

After four years in the Navy, I got my T-shirt and key chain and completed my tour of duty with an eye on a new career path.

I went home and decided to use the G.I. Bill to pursue a Doctorate in Organizational Management and Leadership. I moved to Hattiesburg to be with my girlfriend at the time, and took a job as a sales director and personal trainer at a gym called Anatomies, owned by George Taylor. George mentored me, and to this day, I am grateful for what he taught me about life and health.

For the next three years, I was George's number-one trainer. I finished all my Ph.D. work with a 3.78 GPA. But I'm still one dissertation away from getting that degree. I have enrolled back with the University of Phoenix and in 2022 I will finish my Doctorate in Organizational Management and Leadership! That motivates me!

Working for George was great, but I started planning to spread my wings and open my own gym in my hometown of Canton. I put the plan together, found a few investors, and by the end of 2015, I was in business.

I'm not going to lie, it was harder than I imagined. Carrying the lease was stressful, and going from sales and training to ownership offered a lot of challenges that I thought I was ready for. I wasn't going to throw in the towel.

But the towel got thrown in on me.

4

The Accident

At times, life puts us in situations in which the circumstances help us discover the strengths and other attributes that God has given us. For me, jail is one example. The Navy was another. But I had the biggest challenge of my life ahead that would test everything I had ever learned to that point.

On December 12, 2017, three o'clock in the afternoon, I went out alone to my family's land to hunt deer. It was a beautiful sixty-degree day with hardly a cloud in the sky. I found the tree in which my brother, Matt, and I had built-in tree stands (Lock-On) that are little ledges hammered into the tree about twenty-six feet above the ground. We called the area "The Green Mile." Using brand new ratchet straps, I climbed up the perch and locked onto the stand.

As I settled in, gazing across the fields, I leaned into the straps, trusting them to hold me secure. But I started to hear the unmistakable sound of the metal ratchet and strap coming undone.

It all happened so fast, I couldn't release my rifle in time to grasp onto the tree and hang on. Instead, all I could do was tuck my chin as I fell forward.

THUMP.

My neck and shoulders hit first. I don't remember the next few seconds, or minutes, because I was knocked out cold. When I started coming to, my vision went from black to foggy gray to finally sharing the clarity of my situation. I was laid out on the ground in a hurt of trouble.

I pushed up from the ground and pain like I've never felt before screamed throughout my body. The pain intensified with every passing second. I felt a warm liquid rolling down my face, and feared it was blood. But it was sweat, the profuse kind the body releases when panic sets in. I lay back down in shock.

After a few minutes, I tried to push myself up again, but this time I couldn't. My mind was telling my body to get up, but my body refused. I started to realize just how bad a situation I was in. Life-threatening at best. Death at worst. I started praying to God, begging for my life. "Please let me live. Please give me strength."

I've got to be 100 percent honest here. I thought I was about to die. My mind was foggy from being concussed, but slowly it started to work somewhat again. Then I had a decision to make: live or die. I chose to fight for my life and at that point, I could feel my will to survive bubble up.

I grabbed my knife off my hip and cut off my gun and backpack. I crawled ten feet to the ladder part of the tree stand and pulled myself up. By this time, I knew I was in deep trouble. In addition to the pain and inability to move, I was having a hard time breathing. I thought my back was going to explode. My right knee was shooting pain throughout my leg too.

In a blur, I managed to limp 400 yards back to my truck. Every step sent pain messages from head to toe. I heaped myself into the truck, turned on the ignition and started driving back home, about eight miles away. With trembling hands, I called Matt.

"Where you at?"

"At home," Matt said.

"I fell from the Green Mile and I'm coming in hot."

"Holy shit! Where are you now?"

"About five miles out."

"Okay. Just get here in one piece," he said.

I pulled in the driveway, stopped the truck and slid to the passenger side. Matt hopped in and started driving me to the Merit Emergency Room Hospital off the interstate in Canton.

Thank God, the ER was a short drive because I could tell my legs were going numb, while pain was shooting through my neck and back. I felt paralysis occurring. Any longer of a drive, and I wouldn't be alive to tell this story.

Upon arrival, Matt helped me through the ER doorway. By that point, everything was a haze. I don't remember much after that as I was injected with morphine. I spent eight hours being examined and treated by the ER doctors. From there, they decided to move me to the University Medical Center (UMC) to be diagnosed by the neurosurgery team.

After one week, I was recovering to the point that I could understand what was going on, able to listen and speak without the high doses of morphine. The doctor came into my room.

"Mr. Walker, it's a miracle you're still alive. And it's a miracle you're not paralyzed," he said, staring into my eyes. "Do you understand what I'm saying?"

"Yes sir, I do."

"But I have to tell you, you may not be able to function like you did before the accident," he said. "Here's why, you have a broken back, broken tailbone, three broken ribs, ligament damage in your hips, a hyperextended knee, and a concussion."

In other words, that fall kicked my ass.

"You're lucky to be alive because the broken vertebrae in your back did not cut or puncture the spinal column. But it is causing a lot of nerve pain."

Even on morphine, he didn't have to tell me that. Still, no amount of pain could hide the fact that a miracle had taken place. Nobody survives landing on their neck after a thirty-foot fall.

"Thanks for being honest with me, doc. What's the plan?"

"We're going to keep you here another week or so to monitor how you respond to the work we've done while you've been under. Then, if all goes well, you'll be released to continue rehabilitation from home."

I gave him a thumbs-up signal with my right hand, and he left.

For the next week my mother, Shirley Marshall, stayed by my side watching as the morphine levels were reduced daily, which meant I had to learn how to deal with the incredible, increasing amount of pain. Then I got the green light to be released.

Before my mom wheeled me out to the car, my doctor stopped in for a final visit.

"Hello Anson, I just wanted to drop by to wish you good luck, and to offer one last way I can help."

"What's that?"

"Well, realistically, you may not recover fully from this, which could set you back for a while if not forever. I could sign a few documents that would put you on disability so the government would send money every month."

I looked up at him eye-to-eye. "Doc, you're wrong. Just watch and see."

----

6 Ways to Win in Tough Times

In tough times, winners find out two things:

1. *Who they are.*
2. *What they are made of.*

In his book Unforgettable, author Jack Kinder phrases it like this: "You are not made in a crisis — you're revealed. When you squeeze an orange, you get orange juice. When you squeeze a lemon, you get lemon juice. When a human being gets squeezed, you get what is inside — positive or negative."

I'll add this — when you get squeezed, when you face serious adversity, a winner will rise up, actually excel in the situation, and a loser will fold like a cheap suit, every time. I've witnessed both. Life is filled with adversity or opportunity, and winners simply see the opportunity!

The best way to approach tough times is to attempt to see them as opportunities, not obstacles. This is a mindset. Most people want their problems to be fixed without having to face them. I don't care if it's financial, marriage, business, health, etc. I see it all the time. Tough people look for solutions. When your people, staff, and family need help, you must take responsibility to make things better. They need help, which you can give them in the form of advice, encouragement, positive reinforcement, and my personal favorite, leading by example.

Here are six things tough people do to win in tough times.

1. ***Define Reality*** *— Peter Drucker states, "A time of turbulence is a dangerous time, but it's greatest danger is to deny reality." My job is to define reality for people. When you are forty pounds overweight, you*

39

will need to work on eating clean food and show up at the gym five days a week. This has to be a top priority or it won't work. It's like this, "Either you deal with what is the reality, or you can be sure that the reality is going to deal with you!"

2. ***See the Big Picture*** *— Tough people are the keepers and communicators of the vision. My job is to remind people of why they are doing what they do and the benefits that await them as a reward for their hard work. Example: The Walker Lifestyle will increase your energy, sex drive, strength, and stamina and will improve your mental focus, overall self-esteem, and confidence. It will lower body fat, anxiety, and stress. I have realized these benefits in my own life and among my clients all the time. I certainly don't want to portray to you that it's easy, because it's not, which is why most people don't do it. But dad-gum is it worth it? YES, 100 percent unequivocally yes. I often don't know all the answers, but I know there are answers, and I'll do everything in my power to make sure we find out what they are. That gives people hope.*

3. ***Develop a Plan*** *— Wherever you are in life right now, before you can develop a strategy to get out of a difficult situation, you must know where you are and where you want to go. You have to identify the steps required to go from here to there. Sounds simple, right? Most people don't do it. My job is to come alongside you and develop that plan.*

4. ***Make Good Choices*** *— People's choices define who they are and where they are going. It's true we don't choose everything we get in life, but much of what we get comes from what we've chosen. From a personal standpoint, the overall quality of my life dramatically increases in proportion to the good decisions I make. I'm talking about every aspect — financially, relationally, business, spiritually, emotionally, mentally, and physically have all increased. I also speak from experience from the other side. If there was a bad choice to be made, I have made it. I've lived with the consequences of bad choices for a long time. Trust me when I tell you, make good choices. Make smart choices and do the*

right thing and I promise you won't regret it!

5. **Promote Teamwork** — *I think this is one of the hardest concepts for many people to grasp in the "me, instant gratification" society we live in today. No team can win and keep winning unless everyone works together. Your job as a winner is to promote teamwork and help lead people to cooperate and work together. We need more Indians and fewer chiefs. I promise if you take this approach, when your team, company, or organization wins, you will too. You'll get more personal accolades than you can count. I've seen it, and I've participated in it. It has happened to me over and over and over.*

6. **Be Hopeful** — *Hope is the foundation of change. In this case, I'm talking about you personally, mentally, physically, and emotionally. If we continue to hold hope high and help others do the same, there is always a chance to move forward and succeed.*

I know we live in difficult times. Difficult times call for discipline. Discipline gets you paid. Complacency gets you in trouble. As winners in life, our job is to be active when facing challenges, break through obstacles, put out fires, correct mistakes, and help people. When your effectiveness becomes contagious, it will spread through your family, your team, and your company. Guess what happens? Positive results!

Enough's Enough

That day, after my mom settled me in at my apartment where I was going to recuperate, the best I could do was return to my bed, basically a motionless zombie. My confidence all but disappeared. I was wallowing in self-pity, pain, opioids, and alcohol. I couldn't sleep more than two hours at a time because my back would hurt from the compression of my weight. When I did fall asleep, I'd have the same horrifying nightmare of falling from the tree. Every day cycled like it was from the movie *Groundhog Day*. The doctor could add one more diagnosis — Post-Traumatic Stress Disorder.

I actually remember the first time the alarm clock woke me up after my accident. I managed to sleep almost four hours. It scared me. But I smiled. I never imagined recovering from my accident would be so hard. Time and again, it made me realize the gifts God has blessed us with, like the gift of pain-free health. Let me talk about pain.

First, physical pain: If you haven't experienced nerve pain, let me tell you it's immobilizing — sort of like getting hit in the nut sack. My broken back sent nerve pain throughout my upper body, while my broken hip sent nerve pain down my lower body. Every breath was hindered by the broken rib cage, which caused pain every time I breathed in air. I was downright miserable.

Second, mental pain: Saying it was difficult to remain positive is a massive understatement. Without being able to manage my business, I had to let my gym go. I built that gym with my bare hands, but I had to cancel the lease, let my clients know I was unavailable, and have the equipment moved into storage. I felt like I had lost it all, and not surprisingly, depression set in. What was I supposed to do? Every day I had to answer the question, *Should I give up?*

It was like being in jail all over again, only worse. At least in jail I could get outside and play ball with the fellas. I had my health, and I didn't have this kind of pain.

Gingerly, I was able to get on my feet and move in slow-motion. After two months, I had a moment I call "blonde clarity." I figured if I could stand, walk, and talk, I could make a difference in someone else's health while making some money.

I hooked up with a childhood friend who owned Starke Fitness. I assured him I would do my best to help his business by training individuals.Gritting through the pain, I was able to take on a personal training job at Starke Fitness in February. It wasn't even remotely easy. Every day was an incredible challenge. I took opioids every four hours for the pain. But at least I was helping others, and that felt good. On Fridays and Saturdays, I would drink Vodka along with the pain pills to make myself pass out, attempting to sleep for a few hours at a time. This was no way to live, I can assure you.

A few weeks passed, and it was mid-February 2018 on a Saturday night — two months after my accident. I finished training at the gym, popped a few pills, washing them down with vodka. I grilled up some dinner for my dad and me, then settled into my Lay-Z-Boy chair with the bottle in my hand. After my dad went to his room to sleep, I sat with the lights on, no TV, just leaning back, getting sloppier in a drunken stupor while staring into space.

"Anson," a voice inside me called incredibly loudly. I believe it was God Almighty, even if the next words wouldn't be said in church. "What in the hell are you doing? Get your shit together man. You know what to do! NOW DO IT!"

Scared straight, I stood up and thought, *Enough's enough.* I grabbed all my pain pills and threw them in the firepit outside. Next, I poured out all the vodka. Now it was just me and my Maker.

For the next six months, I went back to training without the crutches of opioid pain medications and alcohol.

I'm convinced this allowed my body and my mind to heal faster. I dedicated myself to finding a way to heal my back and my body. I forced myself to face the pain and began my physical, emotional, and now spiritual, recovery.

Instead of treating adversity as a tombstone,

43

look at adversity as a stepping-stone.
— *Anson-ism*

One of the first things I did was to lie flat on my back on top of an ab mat to let my back get used to my body weight. Then I designed a series of flexibility kicks to strengthen my hamstrings and lower back. I used an ab ball for more exercises because it took pressure off my back. Gradually, I started healing and getting stronger.

Soon, I assumed the role of Director of Training, and I could feel myself getting my act together. I started working harder and smarter. I became more productive than I'd ever been in my life. But by far the greatest revelation for me during this time is that it's not about me.

John Maxwell is my favorite author. There's not even a close second. He has a saying, "People don't care how much you know until they know how much you care." And brother, that's the truth. That's the best advice I've ever used in the last three to four years, that right there. When you legitimately care, people can tell. They appreciate when we take the time and energy to listen without giving advice. The act of being available to care for others is powerful for both you and the one you care about. It goes both ways. Something deeper happens, like building trust and respect. When I started living with this attitude, I became curious about people. I wanted to learn what makes people tick. In turn, when they were willing, they listened to me too. A major shift began to happen in my business, heading in the right direction.

This is also when I realized I was onto something with my lifestyle habits and what I'd learned over the years. I recognized that I could relate to all kinds of people. My story gives people hope. My lifestyle models hope, and my approach makes fitness fun.

Eighteen months after the accident, I remember driving from the gym and realizing my back didn't hurt. After experiencing pain every second, every minute, and every hour of the day for more than a year, I was startled with the unmistakable feeling of NOT being in pain. Tears of joy welled up in my eyes.

"Thank you God!" I didn't think I'd ever live without pain. It was my new normal. But at that moment, hope filled my soul. I wasn't going to ever give up becoming the best version of myself that I could be.

After two years, I went back to the hospital to visit the doctor who offered to put me on disability. I'll never forget the look on his face when he saw me. His mouth hit the floor in shock. He never could have imagined, or believed, that I was every bit as strong as I was before the accident.

Now, at the age of forty-seven, I can honestly say I'm stronger than I have ever been in my life. I may not be able to run and jump like I used to, but I've got strength that comes from above, from within, and from never giving up.

Looking back, the accident was another gift from God. I may have lost my gym, but I also lost the stresses of having to pay that monthly lease and operate it on my own. No longer did I have to worry about operating, and profiting, from the gym business. I learned that my greatest strength is training individuals. That's what I'm designed to do — to help others enjoy the benefits of what life has taught me through The Walker Lifestyle.

II

Health Reborn

5

Walking The Walker Lifestyle

I wake up every morning at 3:15 a.m., except on weekends when I catch up on rest. But my day actually starts the night before at around 8 p.m., when I go to bed and start reading. I never make it past 9 p.m. I'm programmed. It's just a habit.

After my alarm goes off, I'm always grateful. Grateful to be alive. Grateful not to be in jail. Grateful to have a life that God designed for me. Grateful to be able to share my gifts with others. Grateful to be a catalyst for transformation in my clients. Grateful for the opportunities life presents. It's a new day, and I'm happier than a mule eating ice cream.

Typically, I pack a sack lunch and get to the gym by 4:15 a.m. to open up and spend fifteen minutes reading the Bible. My first clients arrive at 4:30 a.m. I'm training folks until noon, and then I have a fifty-minute window for my own workout. I drink a protein shake, and by 1:00 p.m. I'm either returning to train clients, or I've got the rest of the day to take care of administration, writing my radio segments, making meal or fitness plans, and sending emails. By dinner time, I've improved on yesterday — whether I've gained more physical strength, mental toughness, spiritual enlightenment, or emotional balance. That's my lifestyle. It works for me. Trust me, it's a whole lot better than being locked in a cell or tied to a hospital bed hooked to an IV. I couldn't do it if I lived on Cheetos and Ho-Hos and sat on the couch all day.

> **"Being on time is late.**
> **Being early is on time."**
> **— Dan Walker Rule**

I'm not trying to be the next anybody, or compete with anybody. I'm just trying to be the best me. It's me versus me. I don't expect you or my clients to start their days at 3:15 a.m. But I can tell you right now, I'm better right now, at 1:20 p.m. Central Standard Time than I was at 1:20 p.m. Central Standard time yesterday. Because I worked out, and I trained clients. I have gotten stronger. I got smarter. I read about thirty pages in my book last night. So each day I'm competing against myself. And I just want to be a better me. I think people miss the boat on this. This is not selfish. Being the best Anson Walker allows me to help my clients at a higher level, to help my fiance at a higher level, to help my family at a higher level. It allows me to perform at a higher level in all aspects of my life. And that's what The Walker Lifestyle's about, to perform at your best possible level. You versus you. To be a better version of yourself every day moving forward.

The Walker Lifestyle isn't about how early you start your day — although you will get more accomplished if you start the day earlier. It is about focusing your energies on today, from start to finish. For today only, how did you do? How do you feel? What have you learned? What have you gained in strength or lost in fat? If you can check off these boxes, you're growing. You're improving. You're becoming the best you can be.

You may ask, "Isn't becoming my best just another selfish dream?"

No, I assure you it's not. The more I live out The Walker Lifestyle,

I realize the end result is that I'm becoming selfless. It takes humility to recognize you can improve. Improving yourself allows you to be selfless so you can be of better service to others, a better parent, spouse, or human being. If your people or the people you're connected with in some form or fashion are winning, you're going to win. You're going to win big. That's what we've got to wrap our little pea brains around.

Along the way, we have fun. I don't take myself too seriously because I know I'm human. I make fun of myself. Some clients call me "Ken," because of my blonde hair, blue eyes, and posture. But I don't mind. They know I'll dish it out too, but it's all in good fun. If it's not fun, then you might as well throw The Walker Lifestyle out the window. It's not going to happen. Nobody wins if this lifestyle is a drag. You're not getting better and neither will those in your life.

Of course, The Walker Lifestyle involves the food we eat and the exercise we do. But it also includes how we think and how we feel. The bottom line is that The Walker Lifestyle is just a series of habits, with built-in flexibility or grace. But it starts with the body we've been given. God made our bodies to work — which is not a dirty four-letter word. Here's why. Unlike an engine that gets a certain number of miles before it wears out, the more we use our bodies, the better they get. We just have to hold up our end of the bargain. From a fitness standpoint, daily activity means everything. It could be thirty minutes. It could be forty-five minutes. It could be two hours or more. It doesn't have to be at the gym. You've just got to be active. You've got to get your butt off the couch and get moving.

In order to keep moving, we have to fuel our engines with quality, high-octane material. Would you fuel a jet plane with Kool-Aid? No, you'd want to put in the best fuel possible. Yet our bodies are more valuable than a jet plane. We've got an incredible system. A body, mind, and soul that work together. So staying active is one piece to the puzzle. We have to feed the mind, body, and soul with equal care and quality. I believe we have to commit to absorbing material that lifts us up rather than dragging us down.

Another piece of The Walker Lifestyle that is really, really important is about surrounding yourself with people who are going up. I don't hang around negative people. I can't. Because my mental health depends on the fact that I hang around mentally healthy people. Yes, I love all people, but I don't have to associate with anyone who is on a losing path with a toxic attitude.

When you put these pieces together, you're going to get what you want, times ten. Taking care of your mind, body, and soul and helping others become successful will deliver rewards beyond your expectations. In a nutshell, that's what The Walker Lifestyle is all about. A way of life that delivers positive results for yourself and others.

Before we talk about exercise and nutrition, I believe we must get our priorities in order. I don't want to offend anyone, but if you're coming to me, or reading this book, you are asking me for help because something in your life is not working. Maybe you're overweight. I'd say you haven't made fueling your body a priority. Maybe you're out of shape. Then you haven't taken your fitness seriously. Maybe your relationships aren't working. Well there's a chance something's out of order in your life.

I suggest trying the following exercise on your own. Write down your current priorities in life. Then write a list of what you would like your priorities to be. Then compare the two lists. The more you can veer towards your preferred priorities, the better.

For example, I'm going to lay out my top five priorities, which are the backbone for my life and which help me manage my time, efforts, and energies.

Anson Walker's Priorities At-a-Glance

1. Relationship with God
2. Relationship with Yourself
3. Relationships with Your Family, Friends, and Loved Ones
4. Your Career / Work
5. Living by Your Values

Every day I see people who I can tell have their priorities mixed up and aren't living by respectful values. It's not hard to miss. Especially down here in the South where drinking beer, eating fried foods, and sitting on a couch seem to be priorities to people. I'll even have clients come to me and tell me they've got their workout plans all figured out. They jump on the treadmill for a few minutes and hit the showers. I'm not trying to embarrass anyone, but if you got it all figured out, how come you're still fifty pounds overweight? But if they're willing to surrender control and work with me for thirty days, rearranging a few priorities, life is going to change for them and for the better. I assure you of that.

Here's how I break down my priorities.

No. 1 — Relationship with God

Before skipping this section, take an honest inventory of what you believe in. You'll get my answer in this section. But I suggest beginning — if you haven't already — a journey to explore a power greater than yourself. Our will, human will, can only get us so far, and it can fail us. That's why I put my faith in God as my higher power because I know Anson, and he can let himself down.

I believe that people are either very ignorant or very arrogant if they don't believe there's a God. All I have to do is walk outside and take a breath of fresh air to realize we didn't do this. The more we work at The Walker Lifestyle, and in our faith in God, the younger we actually get and the longer we live. Anything man-made has a shelf life. So I have to acknowledge that as a human race, we're still figuring out the laws of the universe. But somebody has already figured them out because they're here and active. I choose to trust in him.

I deal with a lot of people who have initials after their names. In my experience, it seems like the more degrees somebody gets, the more arrogant they are. I think arrogance is one of our biggest enemies. The higher people get on the education scale, the more atheist they become. I'm not sure why that happens, but that's my perception because that's what I've lived.

I've questioned God at different times in my life. I've questioned if there is a God, and I always come to the same conclusion — that without a doubt, 100 percent unequivocally, there is a God. And the fact that he gives us the opportunity to choose him and accept his relationship or go on our own tells me just how much he loves us. He gives us that choice.

Since God is my top priority, it plays out in my daily life all day long. My day always begins with some kind of quiet time, or devotional reading, with God. It sets my priority on top from the get-go. I'll read the Bible many days. That's one book that never goes out of style. After all, it was written 2,000 years ago and continues to be a bestseller. When I read it, the words seem to come alive and resonate with my soul. When I put it all together, even from a common sense standpoint, not a Christian viewpoint or an atheist viewpoint, there's something there to acknowledge and that's relevant to life.

By making God my top priority, I fall under his leadership. I want to live by his rules and experience the fruit of that labor — love, joy, peace, patience, kindness, among others. As my top priority, I try to stay connected with him through the day. I'll send up little prayers all the time. I trust he's listening because he loves me. I want to be a better man, and God gives me the road map and encouragement. So

I'm not playing for Anson Walker. I'm playing for Jesus Christ. That's my coach, and that's my captain.

When I was growing up, I thought of Jesus as a soft, meek man who was borderline feminine. As I got older, I realized what an absolute man's man he was. When they were torturing him, he could have squashed them in two seconds. But he didn't. He had a purpose to serve — to save humanity. He took the beatings while loving those around him in the process. That's the ultimate man move.

In my life, I try to model that kind of sacrifice and love for others.

Here's the thing I've learned: somebody is always watching you and me. Whether it's our kids, colleagues, or people in the grocery store. They are watching. Most of the time, they are quick to judge. So by making God my top priority, I answer to him and try to please him. What people see is a man trying to be his best, and that speaks volumes.

No. 2 — Relationship with Yourself

I've experienced the fact that when you fix yourself first, you'll watch your world change. In other words, love yourself so you can love others.

As you've read, back in my late twenties I was partying all the time, drinking too much, and chasing women around. I wasn't taking myself seriously. I was out for pleasure, and that was my top priority. Every time I did that, I woke up in the morning feeling guilty. I wasn't taking care of myself. I was being selfish, in a bad way. You know the story, it drove me into a 12' x 12' jail cell.

My second priority can be summed up with The Walker Lifestyle. It's taking care of your mind, body, and soul so you can be at your best. It's so important.

Taking care of yourself includes what you put into your mind. This means avoiding trash TV and entertainment, associating with negative people, and virtually anything else that doesn't add anything positive.

It's hard to be positive if you're feeding your mind with negativity.

Taking care of your body also helps care for your mental health. Exercise has a way of making you feel good about yourself and who you are becoming. Seeing and feeling progress leads to positivity. It just does. I'm also more productive when I'm on a systematic regimen that cares for my whole self every day. I get so much more done. I take care of myself. I take care of my fiance, Tiffany. I take care of my responsibilities. Discipline is a by-product. And discipline gives me freedom to be more, do more, and love more.

No. 3 — Relationship with Others

I've said it already, but if we help ourselves, we will end up helping others. This includes your spouse, family, and friends. Who we love and how we love them becomes my next highest priority. That's how I'll be remembered.

If I'm lazy and put my lifestyle on hold, it's one of the worst things I can do to myself and others. That's when I can get myself in trouble mentally. But if I'm healthy as a horse, I've got a lot more energy. I've got a lot more compassion that I can give other people. So I choose to invest in myself so I can give time and energy in return to those around me. People play a huge part in our development, and ultimately success. So learning to be a servant leader, or a happy helper, or just someone who cares for others will go a long way. As I've said, people don't care how much you know until they know that you care.

No. 4 — Your Career / Work

First, notice that my career is not even close to being my top priority, or second, or even third for that matter. Sure, it's important because I have to pay the bills and be prepared for what the future brings. But putting career ahead of God, yourself, and others will eventually run you into the ground.

I believe we have to put work in the right perspective. Being successful is the result of getting the first three priorities right. Work is not the end-all. If you make work that high of a priority, you will use people, and it will cost your health in the process.

If I put my career number one, my relationship with Tiffany would go to crap. I would never see my family. I think I would be sad. I see too many people with their job as number one and everything else is third. Their marriages suck. Their kids don't know them. They may know Daddy or Mommy pays for this, this, and this, but they don't get the full value of knowing their parent. The older I get, the more I realize there are moments in time that you can't get back. Time is more valuable than money because we can never get time back, but we can get more money.

Everything else gets out of whack if we put work as top priority. It's like taking a prescription drug, because there are always four or five bad side effects. If I'm not happy inside, I'm not going to be fully available to help anybody else or be productive at work. If you have a healthy mind, body, and soul, then you're probably going to be pretty good at work too. That's just the way I view it, and it's worked for me.

I think you have to love what you do too. I really do. I love health. I love nutrition. I love mental, physical, and emotional fitness. All of that is right up my alley. And I think I found a pretty good formula for success. But the juice is helping others achieve success. If I do that, we both win.

----

4 Ways to Living Your Values

Hopefully you have narrowed down a list of values that you intend to stand for. A few of mine are honor, integrity, and commitment. But knowledge and intention are not enough. You have to live out your values every day. It takes discipline to establish and incorporate strict values that you live by daily. Then it will eventually become a habit. Work them until you don't even have to think about it!

Here are four things that help me be consistent with The Walker Lifestyle values.

1. ***Embrace Your Values*** *— Begin every day by reminding yourself of your values. Then, as you face decisions throughout the day, honor those values with every decision you make. If the opportunity presents itself, tell others why you made the choice you did. It adds credibility to you with your peers, kids, players, students, etc., and it cements your values in your mind and helps you practice them. It also adds another level of accountability for you. That's powerful, my friends.*

2. ***Your Actions Must Equal or Exceed Your Values*** *— Discord between values and actions erects chaos in a person's life. If you talk about your values but neglect to walk them, then you will continually undermine your integrity and credibility. I read this statement once, "Fake it until you make it." I couldn't disagree more. That's not living with integrity and it's a lie. Instead, work your fanny off until you make it. Then work even harder because now you have more to give. Take the time to compare every action you take with your values. They better match! If your actions don't match your values, you have lost. People can spot a phony ten miles off. Knowing this has helped me make better decisions in the last eighteen years of my life. Now I know the decisions I make*

today will be solid. I can promise you that! If and when you screw up, own it. Admit it. Come clean.

3. ***Don't Waiver*** *— When times are tough, stick to your values. When you're feeling good and everything is going your way, it's not hard to implement and live by your values. However, when your values require you to take a stand or do something that will cost you financially or hurt your relationships, feelings such as anger, fear of consequences, or unknown reactions can make it harder to follow through the way you want. Anyone can do it when it's easy. I want to be in the trenches with the front line troops, or the recovering drug and alcohol addicts, because they have been through hell and made it through even better as people. Handouts are for the weak. Entitlement is for losers. Nobody owes you a thing! Take a deep breath, pause, pray, give it some time, and resolve to prioritize your values over your feelings in every decision. You have to do the right thing. Winners make the hard decisions. Winners give the tough love and hope their feelings follow suit.*

4. ***Evaluate Yourself Daily*** *— Be honest with yourself or you're going to fail yourself. Ben Franklin used to get up each morning and ask, "What good will I do today?" When he went to bed, he asked himself, "What good did I do today?" He was essentially evaluating himself daily. Winners focus on their responsibilities, not their rights. Just because you have the right to do something doesn't mean it's the right thing to do. Change your focus from rights to responsibilities and two things will happen: (1) you will gain maturity and wisdom, and (2) you'll start winning in life at a rapid pace.*

No. 5 — Living by Your Values

My fifth priority wraps up all the other priorities. It's about being a man or woman of character, who lives by a code of conduct. These principles include things like being honest, being true to your word, having discipline, and being consistent with your effort and attitude. To me, if the fifth priority is a hobby, cars, or some other entertainment, then you're putting the pursuit of pleasure ahead of something incredibly critical.

Your values define who you are, and that's what you want people to remember about you. I want people to recognize my name with a value attached, like "he's someone who genuinely cares about the health of others." If they remember me as the convict, or just another trainer, then I've missed the target. Or they may say I'm the guy who recovered from nearly dying by falling out of a tree, but they will never say that Anson Walker lied to me.

> *"Your word is a contract. Never lie.*
> *Lying, stealing, and cheating are all the same."*
> *— Dan Walker Rule*

I want to be known for being compassionate, kind, and fair — especially loving. Maybe funny too. The point is to make my life about something more than just making a living. How I treat people — regardless of the situation — is a reflection of the values that run my life. These values are always on my radar, and they prevent me from becoming like "the old Anson," whose selfishness drove him into an orange jumpsuit.

People tend to overanalyze life sometimes. Let me simplify this point by saying this: Work hard, play hard? I'll take it one step further.

- Worship hard.
- Love hard.
- Rest hard.

- Work hard.
- Live hard.
- Try hard.

What I mean by that is to try your best at everything. Why not? It's just going to make you a better person, and somebody people will respect. Anything less is just letting yourself down. If you're not going to try hard, take your kickball and go home. But if you have this attitude and approach, you're going to have an unbelievable life. It's that easy.

6

Ground Rules of The Walker Lifestyle

People always ask me basically the same question in different ways, "How are you going to help me lose weight?" Or, "What's your plan and how does it compare to others?" Or, "Should I be on the 'X' or 'Y' diet?" Or, "I've tried them all [diets] and I cannot seem to get ahead. What am I doing wrong?"

They all have the same answer: The Walker Lifestyle.

I'm not going to make you weigh-out your food portions or suggest intermittent fasting, or go Mediterranean with your diet, or train like a bodybuilder, or run like a marathoner. These all have merits, but they don't fit everybody. They're short-term solutions to a long-term lifestyle problem. There's really no single shortcut or secret that nobody is telling you. Instead, I offer principles for success that can be sustained forever.

I call these principles "ground rules" because I've always thought that to win at something you have to know the rules of the game. In this game, we want to be our best physically, mentally, emotionally, and spiritually. And this is one game where a little cheating will only hurt yourself and your progress.

I've tried just about everything with fitness and dieting. I tell all my clients, I'm the guinea pig. Everything you can think of, I've done it. I'm going to tell you what works and what doesn't work from personal experience. You don't need to buy a six-pack abs package from an infomercial. The fact is, we've all got a six-pack of abs, they are just underneath a layer of fat.

Assuming you've taken inventory of your priorities, and made some adjustments, the next step is to learn the ground rules and stay within the boundaries the best you can. The good news is that it's not rocket science. Just common sense.

You're not going to take one step in the gym or make any progress at all unless you've tackled your mindset. Every day will bring new challenges, and excuses for not following the ground rules. So I believe the mindset comes first. Then it's all downhill from there.

So let's get started with a check-up from the neck-up.

Find Your Motivation

Whether you're thinking about starting or have been living healthy for years, everyone must be motivated in order to make changes. What's going to get you out of bed an hour earlier than normal to work out? What's going to make you choose differently at the grocery store? What's going to keep you disciplined and consistent when it's raining outside, or you feel pain, or you just don't feel like it?

You might as well start with your personal motivation to change. Because if you can't find a reason, there's nothing I can do or say to help. That's the bottom line. That's hard for me to admit, but that's the truth.

Some people are living on a fast-track to the grave. It's sad, but they have not found any motive to help them change. More than one of every four people will die from heart disease, which is largely due to being overweight and out of condition. Down here in Mississippi, I can't tell you how often I come across people who seem to just not care about themselves. Many Southern folks specialize in eating fried foods, drinking beer at every meal, and exercising their behinds on the couch. It's no wonder we have the highest rate of obesity in the entire U.S.A.

What will it take for you to change?

I can't answer that. But I can give you a few ideas:

1. **For your loved ones** — They may not say it, but they want you around a long time. They're concerned about your health.
2. For your performance — To perform your best at work, at home, at your hobby, and in life, you need to be in top condition.
3. **For yourself** — Vanity isn't always a bad thing, especially if you're motivated to fit better into that dress or suit, look better in photographs, and generally be more attractive.
4. **For your health** — I have some clients come to me because their doctor prescribed exercise for them or else their life would be at risk. Or they just "get sick and tired of being sick and tired."
5. **For the fun of it** — Living at your best makes life more enjoyable. It helps attitude and increases hope, confidence, and positivity. Whether or not you enjoy working out, the results are worth it.

Still, some folks give up before getting started. Why? It's their mindset. They've already created failure in their mind, so they stay stuck. I've outlined at least ten ways people sabotage change. Notice that only one of them has to do with taking action. All the others are mental.

10 Ways People Sabotage Positive Change

If five or even ten years down the road I'm not different, I haven't changed, I haven't grown in any areas of my life, I will be disappointed in myself. Change is inevitable. I reflect back on my life, my mental state and physical condition are completely different from twenty years ago, and I'm proud of that. How do people overcome problems, challenges, and difficulties? They make changes, friends. Improvement requires two things: Work and change. Innovation requires change. Seizing opportunities requires viewing something as an opportunity instead of the problem. We all know this, yet most human beings resist change. Why? I have my theories.

Since we know most humans resist change, good teams, good companies, and good families must have great leaders, especially in difficult times. Winners make things happen. They get results. Winners don't talk about doing, they just do. Not only are winners productive individually, they're also able to help their teammates, coworkers, employees be successful as well. They find ways for the team and organizations to win. You see, winners lead themselves first, they are the example, the guinea pig, and others follow. With The Walker Lifestyle, I figured out years ago the best advertisement I could ever have is me. If I'm not in good shape, then what in the hell am I selling?

It bothers me when military personnel or a policeman or fireman or doctor or nurse is significantly overweight. It bothers me for these three reasons. It's unhealthy, it dishonors the uniform, and it dishonors themselves. It's just disrespectful in all areas. I support the blue 100 percent, but your life can depend on your fitness level. I support firemen 100 percent, but someone else's life can depend on your fitness level. You've got to realize it's not just about you.

Winners succeed in leading people through change, and they have a unique perspective on the process. They expect, prepare for, and welcome it. Many

65

people hope for change to happen, but few people want to actually change. If you still eat garbage or eat five cheat meals per week, then you don't want to change your body. There is no other explanation. Well Anson, you might say, "I'm trying." But I would say, "Absolutely not." There is no try. There is only do or there is don't. Try doesn't exist. Just do it! It's not that hard. Everyone can do it. I promise. Throw away the garbage, don't put that crap into your perfect body that God blessed you with.

Friends, when you completely sell out to yourself, commit to 100 percent change, you can't be stopped! Your growth — mentally and physically — can't be stopped. I guess the question is, Why wouldn't you do that? I think many people see commitment as an event. They shake hands to close a business deal. They buy a treadmill in order to exercise. But that's only an impulse. That's not commitment. The commitment is getting started. And you better believe that anytime you make a commitment to something, it will be tested. You will be tempted like you can't imagine! Commitment is a process. Oh, and if and when you decide to change and be committed, get ready for the naysayers. The armchair quarterbacks, the folks sitting in the bleachers distracting you even though they don't have the guts to get on the field and play ball. If that's you, stop it. Be miserable but do it quietly. This health and nutrition and fitness thing is tough enough without your negativity. Leave, you are dismissed. I've dealt with negative significant others my whole career, and it's disheartening. I've also dealt with the opposite from my significant other, and it's downright magical. All on the same team with the same dream. Beautiful.

What do you think is holding you back?

Here are ten ways people hold themselves back from achieving their fitness goals:

1. **Fear** — This includes fear of failure, fear of rejection, fear of ridicule, and fear of disappointment.
2. **Excuses** — Excuses often sound like this: I'm not ready. It's not the

right time. I'm not good enough. I'm too old.

3. **Procrastination** — *Putting things off until next week, next month, next year, and mostly forever. You're not quite sure what you're waiting for, but whatever it is that happens, you'll be ready to begin pursuing your goals. But friends, this day never comes. Your dream stays as nothing but a pipe dream because you refuse to act. Putting things off can only hold you back.*

4. **Lack of belief** — *There is nothing that can stop you as long as you have the belief. Stop letting your lack of belief hold you back.*

5. **Lack of focus** — *Every time you lose focus, it kills your chance of success! Get your priorities in order and your focus will follow. I promise!*

6. **Lack of a big picture** — *For your goals to work for you, they need to help you realize your dreams. Those big dreams. It's only when your goals matter that your goals can inspire you, help you focus and help you make the sacrifices that you need to make, and the strength to overcome obstacles as you pursue your big picture dreams.*

7. **Not having a plan** — *A plan gives you a map toward your goal. Benjamin Franklin once said, "Failure to plan is planning to fail." If you don't have a plan, find an expert to help you draw one up.*

8. **Not taking action** — *You've got to get off the sideline and engage in the game, participate, be active, and win. No action is no progress. It's that simple.*

9. **Not reviewing your progress** — *Anyone who is successful is constantly achieving their goals by consistently reviewing their progress and making adjustments along the way.*

10. **Giving up too soon** — *Friends, we all hit points when it seems like keeping on is next to impossible. Too many people give up when they are on the brink of achieving something significant. Never give up.*

What are you waiting on to make a positive change with your life? Are you waiting for the right time? Then it's now. Are you waiting for God to speak to you? Well, God is using me as your personal messenger to say, "Let's get started!"

_____

Most of the time, the absolute hardest thing there is to overcome with living The Walker Lifestyle is walking out your door. There's a five-minute window required to pack your gym bag and leave the house for the gym. If you can overcome that, then — like I tell my clients — "Just show up, and I'll take care of the rest."

Showing up is 90 percent of the work. The other 10 percent is actually following through with the exercise. But I guarantee, you will never regret a workout after you've finished. Your body is pumped up with endorphins, your mind is clear and ready, and you've accomplished one of your top priorities — so there's a sense of accomplishment. When I'm done I'm grinning ear to ear like a mule eating briar. That's just the way it is. And it's never going to change. When I'm eighty-eight, gumming a biscuit, I'm still going to be working out. That's because out of the 10,000 workouts I've had in my lifetime, I've never regretted one.

> *Out of the 10,000 workouts I've had in my lifetime,*
> *I've never regretted one.*
> *— Anson'ism*

Now how many times did I actually *feel* like working out? Maybe 40 to 50 percent. I'm in shape, and I still don't feel like working out every day. But I get after it regardless, and that's when discipline kicks in. Anybody can be inspired for one day, but can you be disciplined for six months? Which brings me to the next ground rule.

Discipline = Freedom

While motivations can change, and have fleeting levels of influence, discipline is what separates those who win and lose. Although it may sound ironic, I believe that discipline equals freedom. How can discipline — or staying with the routine whether you feel like it or not — have a freedom effect?

I've found the more disciplined I am during the week, the more things I accomplish. It's that simple. The more tasks, the more clients. The more disciplined I am, the more money I make, and then the more freedom I have to relax. The more disciplined I am with my time, the more free time I have to do other things — whether it's create moments with Tiffany, go to Ole Miss football games, go hunting, be with family and friends, write a book, or build a business.

In my own life, I enjoy what I do and often put in more than sixty hours a week. I train hundreds of people, and I encourage thousands of others, but I still have to get in my workouts. What good would a fat personal trainer be? I am my best marketing tool, so I have to keep working at being the best I can be.

But I can tell you, by 2:00 p.m. on Fridays, I get the heck away from the gym to recharge my batteries. I use myself as the example, because I know life has many demands on your time too. How are you supposed to get fit when you're juggling a job, family, and other priorities? I can answer that. Discipline. The more discipline, the more freedom you'll have to accomplish whatever it is in life. It may seem like a backward law, but if you can get yourself to believe, discover, and experience the fact that discipline equals freedom, then your life is going to change dramatically.

Commit Like a Convict — Be Consistent

When I was in jail, I learned real quick that my battle was within. There were moments I wanted to just give up on life, give up on what's important, give up on my friends and family. It can be downright depressing to go down this rabbit hole. But one thing was for sure, I had nowhere to go, not much to do, and very few options. I was forced into a life of consistency.

So the question became, what would I do with myself in this consistent lifestyle? I could continue being a sourpuss who sits around all day doing very little. Or I could make the most of it by controlling my effort and attitude.

That's when I learned that 100 percent of the time I can control two things: my effort and my attitude. If I do a good job of this, then everything else falls in line. But if I let circumstances dictate how I feel or what I do, then I'd never have been able to overcome the challenges in my life. It takes a commitment, like a convict, to be consistent with The Walker Lifestyle. That's why all I ask for is a positive attitude and genuine effort.

Now the good thing is that less than 100 percent effort is okay sometimes. You can still win when your workouts generate less than your best. That's the power of consistency. It's better to be at the gym moving your body than sitting at home eating a bucket of ice cream. Our body will respond to exercise regardless of the effort. But the better the effort, the faster and better results you'll get.

The thing about bad attitudes, however, is they tend to spoil the fun. A bad apple ruins the bushel. There's really no place in The Walker Lifestyle for a bad attitude. Are you really going to wake up on the wrong side of the bed every day? Come on. Let's grow up, Peter Pan. You can sulk at home, but don't bring it out in the open. Nobody wants to be around that crap.

I know it's not always easy. But the more consistent we are the easier it gets — even when people are peeing in your Wheaties. We control our reactions. We can be consistent if we take control back from our emotions and stop allowing others to affect our attitudes.

Stay Positive

If we're in control of our attitudes, how can we stay positive? It's important to answer this because life will throw you curveballs, and people will say and do hurtful things to bring you down. You may not see the kind of results you want right away, which can bring negativity to the surface. Why keep up with The Walker Lifestyle if you're not feeling or looking any better?

Staying positive takes a little motivation, discipline, and commitment to consistency. But it helps a ton if you surround yourself with people who are going up.

As I've said before, I don't hang around negative people. I can't. My mental health depends on the fact that I hang around healthy people. I've had to politely step away from several people in my life who bring me down, including some family. I still love them, but I can't let their attitudes rub off on me. It's just better, and I'm more productive.

Toxic people will drain you dry. They really will. Everything becomes harder whether you're at work, at home, or at play.

We need to monitor our attitudes and what we put into our brain and body. What we eat and what we watch can impact how we feel about life. For example, I can't believe what people are watching on TV these days. There's so much crap out there that we can put into our brain, and guess what comes out? It's not that hard to figure out. I've just about given up on TV, except for some of the old classics. I like *The Andy Griffith Show*, for example. It's wholesome, funny, and always has a subtle lesson to walk away with. I love it when Barney screws up and learns a hard lesson. Or watching Opie do something right and get rewarded. It's positive entertainment that's good for my mind.

What are you reading? Are you online more than engaging in life? Are you online gambling and watching porn? If so, what are you doing with your life? Why spend six hours a day on social media? There are so many distractions out there, and they're distracting us for our money and our time. The result is that it's all bringing us down.

Here's a simple test you can do: Whatever it is you are doing, does it lift your spirit or make you feel dirty? If you're feeling even the slightest bit disgusted, then it affects your ability to be positive. Make sense? So stay positive by hanging out with positive people and taking in positive messages, which brings me to the next ground rule.

Make Friends, Family with Fitness

As you begin to seek out healthy friendships, there's a good place to find plenty of them. The gym! There's something incredible that happens when you start making friends through fitness. There's a synergy between having common goals, common efforts to improve yourself, common obstacles to overcome together. It's like being on the same team, or unit, trying to achieve the same goal with the glue being fitness.

It can be challenging to work out alone. It's hard. It's hard to know what to do, how often, how much, and it's hard to stay motivated. I find that there's motivation in the mix, along with a subtle amount of accountability. That's why I encourage people to do group workouts.

There's a dynamic when "you're in this together." It's special, and it keeps you coming back. You bring something to the group that others admire. People will miss you when you're not there. It's an awesome extension of family.

For the guys, group exercise delivers companionship. It's the camaraderie of the brothers. It's that bro code stuff. We can bust each other's balls for forty-five minutes. Nobody gets a break, even me. They call me "Blondie" and "Ken" or other nicknames, and I love it. I believe it's coming out of love. I do the same with them. Some of us are State fans, some of us are Ole Miss fans, which gives us plenty of material to joke around with. So from a guy standpoint, you get a sense of camaraderie. We're training to be the best we can be, like we're preparing for the NFL draft and encouraging each other every step, every lift, and every visit.

For the ladies, group exercise provides a sense of family. It's a sisterhood at the gym. They're mothers dealing with their husbands, or kids, or some other crisis at home. It's like therapy for me. I've learned so much from my female clients over the years. I'm serious. It's awesome. We get on a group text. There's accountability. But when one of them has a problem, we all try to help. I'm not excluded for being a man. When I have something going on, maybe with my mom, these ladies help me. They're like my sisters. It's just a beautiful thing. I wish more people could experience that. I cannot tell you how much I get from these relationships that build you up. These are brothers and sisters, or family from fitness that we wouldn't have otherwise, even if we don't have anything in common except we're at the same gym. That's just special, dude. It really is.

When you're in battle together, which fitness can feel like sometimes, you draw a closer connection with those in the same fight. Even if they're working their weights and I'm working mine, if we're in the same vicinity, encouraging each other, it's like we're doing this battle together. It's like we're in the trenches together.

Show that You Care

As I mentioned earlier, one of the turning points in my training career happened when I learned the following lesson from John Maxwell: "People don't care how much you know until they know how much you care."

During the 2020 pandemic, many businesses were forced to shut down, including gyms. In March, Lee (the owner of Starke Fitness) and I met to decide what to do. We have a 1.75 million dollar gym and lots of overhead, so closing down and possibly losing the business was very possible. I said, "Give me an hour."

I called my lawyer to ask him about staying open and training members despite the "mandates." He told me the shutdown couldn't be enforced legally. There was no precedent. Then I called the sheriff of Madison County, and other local police offices — all of whom I know personally — to ask if they would enforce the mandate or arrest me.

"Hell no, Anson! Just don't advertise that you're open and keep on trucking."

That's what we did! Instead of closing and losing income, we kept two lights on so we could help people. Crisis averted! We increased our sanitization, maintained social distancing the best we could and encouraged everyone to wear masks. At the time, this was a big deal and gave members a positive outlet instead of staying home and watching all the bad news. When the mandate lifted, we were already on a roll instead of starting from scratch. I'm convinced that going this extra mile during all the shut-downs helped our members know we care for them.

What does this have to do with The Walker Lifestyle? It's just an extension of what we've been talking about. When you care about something or someone, you're willing to go the extra mile. If you care about your fitness, you'll do something about it. If you care about someone, you'll try your best to be of service — even if it's just a pat on the back.

People already assume I know something about fitness, that's why I'm called the trainer. But when they realize that I actually care about them as individuals, things change. They listen more intently. They try harder. They trust me with their health. I don't have to go around parading my certifications, hard-luck story, and awards to build their trust. I just have to ask good questions, and listen.

Caring is such an important principle. If I can get someone to care about themselves and their health, then everything else falls in line. In my role as their personal trainer, the more I demonstrate that I care for my clients, the better the outcomes.

As you can tell by my story, I've been around a lot of different kinds of people. So I have a knack for making connections. Some people respond better when we have conversations through the workout. Others need me to push them, even holler at them. Everybody's different.

I keep an eye on their body language so I can see what movements or stretches are resonating with them. When I'm watching, I can tell if they're in a good or bad mood, if they're getting the exercise benefit, or if they're thinking, "I don't know what this son of bitch is talking about." I can tell if they're scared. I'll say to them, "Breathe, breathe, relax. I'm not going to bite you. I'm not going to scream at you. Come here. Give me a hug, come on, we can do this."

I'm not just counting reps; I'm observing their every move so I can help them be their best. Plus, they begin to tell themselves, "Okay, Anson's a normal guy. He gets me. He listens to me. He's watching."

75

And that's how I win them over, because I listen. I care.

Focus on Fat Loss — Forget about Weight Loss

Now that we've got our mindset ready, we can start talking about the ground rules related to fitness and nutrition. The first thing we have to understand is that we are not interested in weight loss. That's irrelevant. You need to lose that term. Instead, we need to focus on *fat loss*. That's what we're worried about. Fat is what makes our heart work harder than it needs to. Fat is the enemy.

What I care about is building lean muscle. When you do that, fat gets replaced with muscle. The scale may change a little, but the fact is that muscle weighs more than fat. So the scale is not what you want to keep an eye on. Instead, focus on body fat percentage. Body fat percentage will tell you how much fat you have, and how much you need to lose. The body fat percentage is a measure of fitness level, since it is the only body measurement that directly calculates a person's relative body composition without regard to height or weight.

The fountain of youth is building lean muscle. It's a simple concept, but one I have to repeat over and over. If you focus on the scale, you can fool yourself into thinking you're healthy. Being a skinny is not the picture of overall health. Being lean with enough strength and endurance to perform at your best is a better picture of health and longevity. We all have different physiques, but I assure you that we also can look and perform better if we focus on fat loss.

Lose the Booze

Drinking alcohol is a real problem. Our society has made drinking booze a rite of passage and synonymous with having fun. But it's also a killer. I've known and worked with too many alcoholics who have had their lives destroyed by the stuff. There was a time in my own life that I was drowning myself with it.

I wish I could talk y'all out of drinking all the time. But I also admit that I'm not going to win that battle. Heck, I love a cold beer, or a Tito's on the rocks. I just have to reserve those delights for the weekends, and even then, I don't go overboard. If you drink, my advice is to steer clear of booze during the week, and learn to enjoy it a little bit on the weekends. If you do that, you'll win. But if you let alcohol become a daily habit, well, I just warn you that there are dire consequences to health and life overall.

You see, alcohol is the most empty calories we can consume. Nutritionally, it does nothing for you. It's a highly concentrated sugar that gets stored as fat — typically right around the middle. Beer bellies are real. If fat is the enemy, then drinking is its most powerful weapon.

The best advice is to lose the booze altogether. But if you can't or won't, then plan to add 10–15 minutes of extra time on the stair climber machine on the day after you drink. Add cardio to burn off those extra calories. In other words, if you're not going to give it up, then give me something in return. That's doable.

Good Intake = Good Outtake

Food is fuel. The cleaner the better. The better you eat, the better you perform. If you can do this on a regular basis, then you're half-way to your goal. That's my philosophy and it's simple.

Unfortunately, we nuke our nutrition with a bunch of BS diets and ideas. I can tell you that I've tried literally dozens of different approaches.

What did I learn?

There's no such thing as a good diet. Diets are temporary, the results are temporary. But if you learn to eat within the guidelines I give you, then it becomes a lifestyle with results that are permanent. Again, it takes a mindset shift from diet to lifestyle.

When I say "clean" food, I mean food that is 100 percent natural without any added sugars, preservatives, food coloring, and other chemicals. Dr. Mark Hyman says, "Eat food grown on a plant, not made in a plant." That's good advice. If the food you're eating has been processed by human hands, then generally it's considered "processed" with a bunch of stuff the body can't readily use, so it stores it as fat.

Don't get me wrong. I grew up in the South eating my momma's blueberry cheesecake and my grandma's pumpkin pie and lemon box pie. I love pizza. I love buffalo wings. I love French fries. While I can make allowances for these kinds of treats, they are not examples of clean food. If I eat junk, I'm going to perform like it. The higher the quality of fuel, the better the outcomes. The lower the quality, the more you'll feel like you have a food hangover, which is worse in many ways than a hangover from alcohol.

To simplify it further, here are my guidelines for "good intake."

- **Eat lean and green.**
- **The less legs the better.**
- **Use carbs cautiously.**
- **Follow the 80–20 rule.**

Eat lean and green — This refers to lean proteins and fresh green vegetables. Two things happen if you eat this way: (1) Your body gets the protein it needs to build strength and the nutrients it needs for life. (2) You feel full, and you feel better.

Obviously, there are a lot of great fruits and vegetables in different colors. So let "green" just reflect anything grown on a plant. You can eat all the vegetables you want, which is a great way to go. But don't confuse any kind of vegetables you get in a can with being healthy. If it comes in a can, then it's not a part of the plan. I like to say, "The longer the shelf life of the food, the shorter your life."

> *The longer the shelf life of the food, the shorter your life.*
> *— Anson'ism*

Instead, find a farmer's market in your area, or shop around the edges of the grocery story — not in the aisles. I'm amazed at how much junk is sitting on those shelves. So head right or left when you get into the store and cruise the perimeter for food.

The less legs the better — I'm referring to the quality of meat for your body. Typically, fish is going to be the best source because not only does it have protein but it has omega-3 fatty acids, which are great for your heart and brain. Then comes the two-legged poultry, which are great sources of protein. But these days, we have to watch out for the oversized birds that have been raised on steroids and other drugs. As much as possible, try to eat cage-free birds. Lastly comes the four-legged variety, like beef. Venison is the best option among our four-legged friends. Venison is the leanest meat, and can be cooked so that it tastes great.

Down here in Mississippi, we have more deer than humans. So hunting — and cooking — deer is one of my hobbies. There are a few tricks to make deer taste delicious. For example, after I've removed the meat from the bone, I soak that meat in ice water for two days. Then I have a meat tenderizer in my shop that I use, then I remove the fascia from the muscle. This creates a super tender meat that can be cut with a spoon. I make venison spaghetti sauce or chili with it, and oh is it good.

Use carbs cautiously — Contrary to many diets out there, carbs (short for carbohydrates) are not the enemy. Think of protein for muscle recovery, vegetables for nutrition, and carbs for energy. With carbs, however, we don't want to overdo them or eat carbs toward the end of the day when we don't need energy.

Carbs are our fuel source. Our brain and body requires carbs, so it naturally does what it can to keep extra in storage (fat). The body breaks carbs down into sugars that the body can use. So that's why we have to use carbs cautiously. I eat carbs in the morning, like some pineapple, and I bring a peanut butter and jelly sandwich with me to work for some midday energy. But after 3:00 p.m., I focus on replenishing myself with some grilled fish and maybe some grilled asparagus or zucchini — no or low amount of carbs. By the way, if I do have a secret, it's grilling. I love to grill. You can grill just about anything and it'll taste great.

I've tried going without carbs to "lean down," but I felt like a zombie. I couldn't think clearly and could barely function. It was like having a hangover. But remember, carbs are not what dominates your plate. Let salads and vegetables be the most dominant, followed by your protein, and then add a little carbs on the side.

If you're getting with this program and adding daily exercise, then you'll find what works for you pretty quickly. You'll notice when you need to eat an apple for energy, for example.

Now a little word about sugar. That's about the closest thing to your enemy as alcohol. Today, sugar is hidden in so many foods. We have to be aware of sugar because it's empty calories that don't serve a real purpose. So look for alternatives and cook with them. Use Stevia, which is a natural alternative. I like homegrown honey, but don't go crazy with it. And avoid aspartame, which is 100 times sweeter than sugar, and is often found in diet sodas. I honestly don't know how it's still legal. It's bad news. It messes with your mind and your body.

Want to fast-track your fat loss? Try cutting down your sugar intake. You'll be glad you did.

Follow the 80–20 rule — The next guideline is my 80–20 rule. The more you can make it 90–10 the better. Try to eat lean and green 80 percent of the time, every meal. On the weekends, especially if you're working out during the week, you can afford to cheat a little bit. I think the best mindset is to establish a high benchmark, then anything less than that will be okay. So shoot for eating lean and green every day, 365 days a year.

Notice I'm not asking you to count calories every meal or weigh out your food portions. If you're eating lean and green 80 percent of the time, you're going to make progress. Eat too many carbs or too much dessert? Well, you can make it up in the gym the next day. The catch is if you eat too many carbs and do not make it up in the gym. That's when you start to gain fat.

I think we are guilty of over analyzing, when it really is simple. Eat clean and you're going to win. My job is to arm you with these guidelines so you can decide if and when you want to go off the reservation. At least you know the rules.

Within time, you won't really miss eating poorly. You'll appreciate feeling great and seeing the progress, which will motivate you to keep eating lean and green. But I also believe in rewarding yourself.

Sticking with The Walker Lifestyle's rules for nutrition is simple, but it can get boring. I'm not going to lie. The challenge is to try different spices and cooking techniques, although I like grilling. And if you're working out hard all week, eating right and taking care of yourself, there should be a reward built in for you. So set a goal, and when you reach it, treat yourself to some ice cream, or a new pair of pants or a dress.

_____

Pretenders vs. Contenders

There are basically two kinds of people. In my world, I try to make things simple, so I'm not trying to hurt anyone's feelings. This is just the way I see it. You can either be a:

- *Pretender — One is never in a position to win. Why? They have excuses for everything.*
- *Contender — Always in a position to win even if they don't always win. But if they aren't winning, they're failing forward, learning, applying, and winning.*

Characteristics of Pretenders:

- *Fear*
- *Impatience*
- *Denial*
- *Impulsiveness*
- *Deceit*
- *Jealousy*
- *Anger*
- *Insecurity*

Characteristics of Contenders:

- *Faith, belief, spirituality*
- *Family and close friends are a priority*
- *Career with a servant leadership*
- *Embrace your background*
- *Life-long learner*
- *Mental health wellness, emotional strength*
- *Strong physical health*
- *Present, with an aura and natural glow*
- *Selflessness — their character is much larger than their ego*

Which one are you? Contender or Pretender?

In the game we play daily called "life," you're referred to as a Pretender or a Contender. In the more than fifteen years that I've been doing this health and fitness lifestyle, I interpret it the way I see it. I use my God-given abilities to process the information available to me. Every week, I run across Pretenders. However the true Contenders are a little harder to come by, and there are several reasons for that. Every one of us has the potential to be a Contender, to reach our designed level of full effectiveness. I believe we have to get out of our comfort zones daily to do this. Folks, when you realize life is not all about you but it's about the people in it, you start to transcend as a person, as a leader, as a servant, as a transformational leader. Servant leadership status is one of the highest honors and status you can possess in the world today! It's a whole new level of euphoria. That is what I call a legitimate Contender.

You see, Pretenders differ on how they are going to influence. Pretenders seek to use their power or status to gain what they want. They try to impress, intimidate, or simply manipulate or overpower others. Pretenders look for the easy way out or an excuse. I see it all the time. They don't understand humility, accountability, or responsibility. Always, always, always it's an excuse or someone else's fault.

In contrast, Contenders seek to love people to gain influence. Contenders see leadership as a platform for loving people, not for getting their own way. Contenders make the transition from selfish leadership to servant leadership. Y'all following me?

These characteristics and examples apply to every one of us daily. We are all on the same team figuratively and the "the doing the right thing" team literally!

Think about the awesome potential each one of us can reach by putting selfishness above selfish self for the good of the team, company, or organization!

Put the overall goal of the team above the personal needs you may feel entitled to. When you commit to this level of thinking, you will receive more personal recognition and accolades than you can imagine. Your team will develop a synergy that you can't comprehend. When your team or company attains perfect synergy, y'all can't be stopped. You can't be beat! I've lived it! I've witnessed it on different teams — in the Navy, with my clients, etc. It's absolutely incredible.

So are you a Pretender, or are you a Contender who doesn't accept defeat? Contenders may lose a battle or two or three, experience a setback here or there, but they are going to win the war! They will not accept anything less than victory!

Contenders also have a "why!" Do you? What is your why? Your why is your fingerprint, or mark you will leave on this life. Your why is your statement of purpose that describes why you do the work you do and why you live the lifestyle you do. It is your calling. It is your conviction. It is your mission statement. It is a vision of your life and work. You know why your why is so damn important? It forces you to live with integrity because it's not just about you!

Knowing your why, knowing your purpose in life helps you live with honor. People who know their purpose in life know who they are, what they are, and why they are! And when you know yourself, it becomes easier to live a life that is true to your core values! Your code!

My Contender Code

1. ***Control Your Effort and Attitude.*** *You have 100 percent control of your effort and attitude in everything you do. When you show up to work with a bad attitude and lack of effort or poor work ethic, you cheat yourself and your employer. Be optimistic, and work like you care.*
2. ***Be Authentic.*** *Own It. Own your shortcomings and mistakes. Own your attitude and start being coachable. It takes guts, but it's worth it. I have two mentors who I ask for advice regularly, and I read religiously. I'm living the lifestyle by learning, reading, applying . . . repeat.*
3. ***Improve Self-Discipline Now.*** *There are 999 success principles that I have come across in my life from reading and experience. None of them work without self-discipline. As I've said, discipline leads to freedom.*
4. ***Get Out of Your Comfort Zone.*** *I sell a lifestyle. I embrace that. I'll never apologize for it. I'm not selling a $4,000 vacuum cleaner. Y'all work for an incredible company with incredible support. Own it. Live it. Love it. Get excited about it. For me, I'm selling The Walker Lifestyle 24/7. I never turn it off.*
5. ***Lose the Victim Mentality.*** *Put humility before honor. Service before self. Work your ass off and expect nothing extra. No one owes you anything. Get rid of the victim mentality because it's destructive.*
6. ***Hold Yourself Accountable.*** *This is the key to maintaining self-discipline that holds many benefits to your mental and physical health. Use rewards and a system of penalties to keep your workouts on schedule. The result will be that you're better in the classroom, boardroom, and bedroom! Sometimes, this means you "play hurt." I don't mean you*

should try to run a marathon on a sprained ankle, but a sprained ankle doesn't have to prevent you from exercising in other ways.

7. *Be a Servant Leader.* *Model leadership by serving those around you. This is what the most influential person in history did, and it works!*

8. *Be Consistent.* *Never give up, even when you feel your self-discipline and accountability are not working. Most people can't be consistent with exercise for an extended period of time, so prove yourself to be different.*

9. *Process of Elimination.* *We have to get rid of the junk that enters our body and minds, because it tends to wear us down. I call this "living in the matrix" because I want to live at a high level daily, not just exist. So examine and eliminate negative people, distasteful TV shows, internet, social media, pornography, gambling, excessive alcohol, drugs, etc.*

10. *Expect to Win.* *Contenders have positive faith, a special super power because they expect good things. When it doesn't go that way, they don't give up. They expect to learn from it and improve the next time. Every day we can either win or lose, but Contenders turn losses into wins with the right attitude and approach.*

I'm often asked, "How many meals should I eat?" My rule of thumb is that it doesn't matter how many. What matters is what you eat. So eat when you need to. When you need some energy, learn to have some healthy varieties ready — nuts and berries and protein bars are great examples. Just don't go hog wild on snacks.

Personally, I eat something every two to three hours until evening. Here's an example of a typical day for me:

3:45 a.m.Wake up

4:00 a.m.Eat eggs and pineapple

4:15 a.m.Off to the gym, training clients by 4:30 a.m.

6:30 a.m.Eat a protein bar or two

7:15 a.m.First workout

9:00 a.m.Protein shake

11:00 a.m.Peanut butter and jelly sandwich

12:30 p.m.Rotisserie chicken, baked potato chips, apple

2:30 p.m.Second workout — followed by protein shake

6:00 p.m.Dinner — turkey, vegetables

Notice that most of my foods are taken in the first half of the day, and that I put in eight hours by noon. So I need a consistent flow of protein and carbs to push me through the day.

> *You can't out-train a poor diet.*
> *But you can use exercise to make up for lost ground.*
> *— Anson'ism*

If I were to skip breakfast and eat Cheetos for snacks, I wouldn't make it to noon. Then I'd be ravenous and would eat too much of just about anything. Bad formula.

The quality of our nutrition is directly related to the quality of our health. Even if we're working out, we just won't see the kind of results we want if we're eating garbage. The saying is true, "You can't out-train a poor diet."

Strengthen to Lengthen Life

Once you've got your mindset straight and nutrition in place, then we can start talking about exercise. Of all the exercises we need to do, strength-training is the top priority.

There are lots of reasons this is important. I'm not talking about becoming a bodybuilder or training like a professional athlete, but the more we work our muscles, the better shape we will be in the long run. We don't want to age as skinny as a rail, nor do we want to go into our golden years overweight. Plus, I like to ask, "Would you rather look like Ben Johnson (a gold medal winning sprinter) or a marathoner?"

Both require cardiovascular training, but marathoners do not want extra muscle weight so they can run fast for twenty-six miles. The result is they are skinny, and over time all that running is going to cause the kind of wear and tear that causes arthritis in the knees and hips. As they age, they will be in pain and without the strength to do life with any ease.

Instead, we want to train to be like Ben Johnson. He used strength-training to increase his speed, and the result is an impressive physique. As he ages, he will have the strength to get up and move. His musculature will create a long-lasting shape even if his muscles shrink.

Science shows that muscle strength helps you live longer. Researchers from the University of Michigan published a study in the *Journal of Gerontology: Medical Sciences* in which they found people with low muscle strength are 50 percent more likely to die earlier than their stronger peers. "Maintaining muscle strength throughout — and especially in later life — is extremely important for longevity and aging independently," said lead researcher Kate Duchowny.

But what do I see all the time at the gym? You won't believe it. Some people will run on a treadmill for fifteen minutes and then call it quits. Others will come in three days a week and go sit in a sauna for twenty minutes and then go home. That's not a workout, and it is certainly not building strength that lengthens life.

At the end of the day, you've got to move your ass. If you have conviction about doing The Walker Lifestyle, then this includes pushing or pulling weights. That's never going to change even 200 years from now. That's just the bottom line.

> *At the end of the day,*
> *you've got to move your ass.*
> — *Anson 'ism*

I know most people don't know what exercises to do or how to do them, so it's important to get guidance. Once you have the right form, then you can pursue function. Heck, even doing push-ups can be done incorrectly. I've provided a 7-Day Walker Lifestyle Plan in the back of this book to get you started. Beyond that, you'll need to tap into my training online at **thewalkerlifestyle.com** and other workouts based on your level of condition.

Everybody is different, yet everybody benefits from strength training. There are some exercises — or lifts — that I avoid, but overall I like them all. There's benefit whenever you're stressing muscles the right way. That's when they grow and strengthen.

In general, I also avoid exercises that can offer a high risk of injury. I know Olympic lifts are popular in some gyms, but if they are not performed with precision, they can really hurt somebody.

I like dumbbells. I like machines. I like to do a little bit of it all. I love the abdominal balls. They all work. The key is identifying what you need. For example, when you see people who walk hunched over, you might think they need a chiropractor. But there's another reason. They've gone years without stretching and strengthening their hamstrings. Along with the glutes, this group of muscles are the biggest ones we have. Weak hamstrings pull the hip forward, which causes the back and neck to compensate.

Yet many times we go to the gym and start throwing weights around and ignore our hamstrings and glutes. Our legs are what keep us mobile, so they need to be a priority.

Here are four guidelines to keep in mind:

1. **When strength training, exercise a different muscle group each day.** You might do chest and triceps one day. Backs and biceps the next. Leg and shoulders on the next. After a few weeks, switch it up. This gives each muscle group time to rest in between days of activity.

2. **Muscle fatigue is the goal.** You want to stress those muscle groups until they feel like Jell-O. Don't hurt yourself, but make sure you give each muscle group a good test with a series of sets and repetitions in each set. Walking up to a lateral pulldown machine and doing 5 reps at a low weight is not where we're heading. Instead, select a weight that you can do 10–12 times until you fatigue. Then repeat that for a few sets. The amount of weight and number of sets will increase as you strengthen.

3. **Confuse your muscles.** What I mean is to use several exercises for each muscle group. Don't settle on one machine forever. Our body learns how to compensate for activity, so to receive the fastest, best strength training, use the concept coined by Arnold Schwarzenegger, "muscle confusion." If you do the same thing (for example, 4 sets, 12 reps, same weight) then your body quits growing, quits changing because it learns to use just enough to get through it. So what we have to do is trick the muscles into performing at a higher weight, less reps, or a lower weight with higher reps.

4. **Don't be a sore loser.** What I mean is don't let soreness cause you to quit. A little pain means you are making gains. Plus, soreness can be dealt with. By giving each muscle group rest in between workouts, the pain subsides. Soon you'll appreciate feeling a little soreness. It's always harder and a little more painful when you're

starting out, but the level of pain decreases over time. So don't give up because of pain. Now the caveat is if you have severe pain in the joints. That means you may not have done the exercise properly and you may have sustained injury. It's still not a reason to quit, but it's a good excuse to get guidance.

5. **Circuit training is a great default**. If you are short on time and only have a few days a week to train, then exercise each of the muscle groups — which is called a circuit. Go from one exercise to another, then repeat the cycle three times. That will get your entire body moving and benefiting. But I'll be honest with you, circuits may be a great default and you will see some gains, but not like following the first four guidelines above. Two days is better than none. But for faster progress, go four or five times a week.

Cardio: The Great Equalizer

Cardiovascular training (aka cardio) builds endurance. If you do strength-training alone, you will still burn calories but you could get tired walking up a flight of stairs. Cardio is also great for your heart and lungs. So we have to incorporate cardio into our workout regimen. Plus, cardio is the great equalizer. For example, let's say we've had a bit too much to eat or drink the night before, we can burn off some of the toxins and extra calories the next day with cardio. It can correct some of those mistakes. Or if you've added an extra notch to your belt loop recently, cardio will help get you back to where you want to be faster. But it's not meant to be the cure-all for all your workouts. I'd like to see you spend around 30–40 minutes doing strength-training, and 15–30 minutes doing cardio. One hour, and you're done.

The goal with cardio is to burn calories by keeping your heart rate elevated for a period of time, between 15–30 minutes.

What's the best cardio exercise for you? All of them, and any of them. But here are a few tips:

- *Similar to strength-training, be sure to mix it up from day to day.* You never want to give your body a chance to 'settle in' and adapt to an exercise. So you might try walking one day, stair-climbing the next, bike-riding the next, etc.
- *Focus on low-impact versions to avoid long-term problems with your joints.* For example, using a treadmill is easier on your knees and ankles than running on asphalt. Walking fast, or a slight jog, is better than sprinting for your joints.
- *High-intensity vs. low intensity* — High intensity and "interval" training will burn more calories and is harder for your body to adapt to the exercise. Low intensity, like a long, slow walk, doesn't yield the same benefits.
- *Walking is great exercise.* We were made to walk, so it's natural. But try increasing the elevation on the treadmill — walking up a hill — to increase the intensity. You can also try wearing a weighted vest to add intensity.
- *Walk backwards.* Walking backwards engages the leg muscles in a different way. It enhances coordination and balance. Believe me, walk backwards for 5–10 minutes and you will start to feel your butt and hamstrings.

My favorite cardio exercise is stair-climbing. It adds a measure of strength-training, and it's harder to cheat. Even at slow speeds, you're engaging your legs to lift your body weight up to the next stair. It's also killer for your butt and calves. So you're getting stronger and leaner in one motion.

I recommend doing some form of cardio exercise every day for about 15-30 minutes. You don't have to be at the gym for this. You can incorporate fun activities that give you exercise. For me, I love golf. I never got to play growing up because I was in other sports. But I discovered "the greatest game on earth" while stationed in California. Since then, I love getting in a round of golf. I also love to hunt, which includes miles of walking while carrying gear. So you need to find or do what you love to do and just do it more often.

Rest for Recovery

As mentioned with strength-training, you want to give the muscles you train at least 48 hours of rest in between workouts. Here's why: (a) to relieve soreness, and (b) that's when the muscles actually grow.

But rest and recovery incorporates a few keys, which are real game-changers.

1. **Post-workout isolate protein**. Within 30 minutes of training, I always drink an isolate-protein shake, which gives the muscles the building blocks for recovery and growth. After working out, you're not going to be hungry, but your muscles still need protein. That's where the isolate-protein shake comes in. While you're waiting for your next meal, your body can start recovering immediately. The last thing you want to do is work out and then wait a few hours to eat. Do that and you waste the opportunity for growth and recovery because the body will be grasping internally at the muscle mass to try to sustain itself. Lactic acid settles in

and then you feel sore, and not the good kind.

2. **BCAA**. Another important tool of mine are BCAAs, or bio-chain amino acids. This is a protein source that helps your body recover when you're dehydrated. It also has B-6, B-12, potassium, and sodium, which water does not have. It's calorie-free, and it dissolves in water, so I'll gulp down some in the morning to prepare for the onslaught of exercise, and then I keep some with me throughout my workouts. It's like Gatorade on steroids to the third power. Dehydration is the enemy, so by taking BCAAs, you will avoid cramping and support muscle recovery. BCAAs and isolate-protein are two of the best things you can put in your body.

3. **Sleep like you mean it**. Getting enough sleep is so important. We humans need it, but especially if we're training daily. How much do you need? That's highly personal. I only need five quality hours, but my fiance needs at least eight. You probably know by now how much you need. So make sure you're getting that sleep. Otherwise, your workouts won't be as effective and your body won't have the time it needs to recover.

I think most people are scared to push their workouts to the limit. We often don't know or realize how much we can do. So I encourage you to go the extra set, try more weight, go the extra mile, and then use these rest and recovery strategies. Your body will respond, and you'll be surprised at how much you can actually do!

Supplement Success

It's nearly impossible to get all the vitamins and minerals that our body needs daily from eating healthy foods. That's why we use supplements to fill these nutritional gaps. Plus, nutritional supplements help us go farther, faster, and leaner. Supplements are derived from natural sources. They're not medicine, yet they have medicinal values. They have power to propel you in ways you may not have even imagined. I believe in them, but I don't pretend to know everything about every vitamin and mineral either.

The nutraceutical industry is massive, bringing in about $420 billion worldwide every year. There's a supplement for almost anything these days, so you're going to have to do some research and be willing to learn about all the ways God has given us natural medicine.

We all need to start with a quality multivitamin for the essential vitamins and minerals. I take a probiotic for a healthy digestive system and omega-3 fatty acids for my heart and brain. I take magnesium for energy and my heart, and I take potassium, which serves as an electrolyte to prevent muscle cramping. Then I have my isolate protein and BCAAs. You can learn more about my own line at **walkerelitenutrition.com**.

7

Photo Story

I loved fishing with my dad growing up, but little did he know that behind the scenes I was routinely being sexually abused by a friend who joined us on fishing trips.

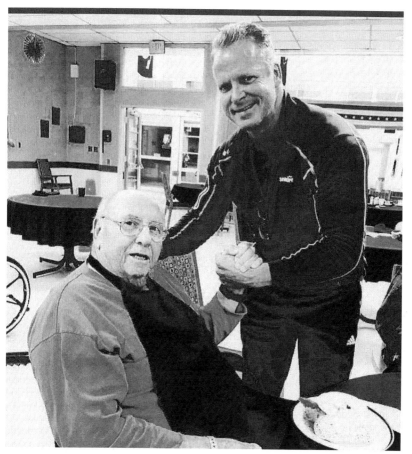

The man behind the Dan Walker Rules before passing November 8, 2020. He was a bad husband but a great father who taught me how not to treat my future wife.

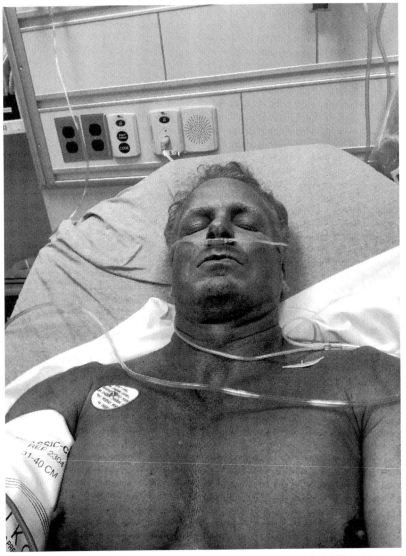

(This is me on Dec 15, 2017 at University Medical Center (UMC) in Jackson , MS after I fell 30-feet upside down. I sustained broken ribs, broken tailbone and a broken back. I'm still pretty scrambled here. I thought I was going to be paralyzed, and knew I was in for a long battle to be normal again.)

This is one of my best friends Hunter Caston. We were riding four-wheelers into the Mississippi sunset.

This is Wendy Smith Montgomery. I trained her for 3 years at Anatomies in Hattiesburg. She is a mother of 3, wife, and now is a personal trainer. She started with me weighing 308 lbs. She now walks around at 155lbs. I am so proud of her. We have been friends for 9 years now.

This is Beth Hutchinson. She's a teacher, mother, wife, and like a younger sister to me. She has been with me for 5 years now. She loves the accountability and the workouts.

This is J.D. Mathis walking unassisted for the first time after a car accident left him paralyzed from the waist down. Read his story in Chapter 8.

This is Steve Tidwell. He was paralyzed by West Nile Virus. I carried him up the stairs to get to the cardio area for a year. He is now walking up the stairs unassisted. Read his story in Chapter 8.

Dr. Sheila Spann went from 208 lbs to 120 lbs. She is now one of my best friends and athletes. I have trained her for 3 years.

Family fun time at the pool with my nieces Mattie Reagan, Mary Tristen and one of their friends.

If I'm not hunting, I'm fishing. Here I am with (from left) Drew Bateman, Brad Ainsworth, and one of my best friends Jeremy Sokovich.

Tiffany is more beautiful on the inside than out. I love you future Mrs.

Walker!

III

Inspiring Freedom

8

Writing the Next Chapter

Everybody has a story, including you — where you were born, how you were raised, favorite memories growing up, tears and heartbreak, accomplishments, challenges, or downright unfortunate circumstances. It all defines who we have become, how we process life, and how we move on. And sometimes our memories distort our stories and our self-esteem. It's easy to blame others and circumstances while holding on to resentment for whatever wrongs that may have happened to you. Life isn't fair, that's for sure. But we don't have to let life — the good and the bad — continue to hold us back from reaching for a better prize.

We can change. We can forgive and let go. We can improve our odds. We can change our attitude, focusing on the positive and taking responsibility for our own roles, hopes, and desires. My story is about second chances. In many respects, I had to learn the hard way. But in each case, the good Lord gave me another chance. Today, I don't take life for granted. Each day is special. Every time I wake up, I'm grateful to be alive. Every time I breathe fresh air, I remember the days locked up smelling nothing but rotten, male-stink. Every time I work out, I'm grateful for the body God has given me. And every time I get to help another, I see opportunity.

But my story isn't finished, and neither is yours. There's still another chapter to write. The only person holding us back is ourselves. How do I know this? I've trained thousands of people, and I believe every one of them has changed for the better in some respect. Still, there are some who have been truly inspirational. It's been an honor serving these folks and a real joy seeing them completely change right in front of my eyes. Their stories are no longer holding them back. Their stories are a part of their history but not their future.

If you ever feel like you need a little inspirational kick, read through one of these true stories written by actual clients.

From Wheelchair to Walking

by Steve Tidwell

- *Age: 61*
- *Weight: 193 lbs.*
- *Resides in: Madison, Mississippi*
- *Occupation: Retired, Union Rep for Kroger employees*
- *Condition: Paralysis from West Nile Virus*
- *Progress: From Leg Pressing 25 lbs. to 118 lbs.*
- *How long with Anson: 1 year, 3 months*
- *Snapshot: Steve contracted the West Nile Virus after being bitten by a mosquito. The virus interrupted his neurological functioning, paralyzing him from the waist down. When insurance stopped paying for his physical therapy, he rolled into my gym in a wheelchair. Today, Steve has regained his strength and relearned how to walk and is now up and able to walk short distances without assistance.*

I was cooking on the grill in the backyard on a Sunday afternoon with my wife sitting nearby. While standing there, I noticed a mosquito bite me on my arm so I smashed it in one swipe. My wife asked, "What was that?" I told her a mosquito bit me. "Well, I'm going in then," because she didn't want to be bitten.

Within twenty-four hours, I started feeling achy, kind of like the flu. My neck and joints hurt. A few days later, I went to the doctor and they tested me for the flu. While I was standing at the end of the table in the doctor's office, I collapsed onto the floor. It was like a light switch just got flipped off inside my body. The doctor turned around and said, "Well, that's not good. We better test for the Rocky Mountain Spotted Fever, Lyme Disease, and West Nile too."

After drawing blood and getting a spinal tap, they ruled out everything but West Nile. I started to lose the ability to move my legs. So we arranged for a nerve conduction test. When the doctor came in, he looked at me and said, "Do you want to know the prognosis, or would you rather not know?"

My wife said, "Yes." But I said, "No," because it didn't make any difference to me; I assumed I was going to walk sooner or later.

"Well, my prognosis is you will never walk again without assistance of some type," he said.

I looked at him and said, "Doc, I'll tell you, you don't know me. I don't give up very easily." And I haven't given up yet.

For the next year I did physical therapy, occupational therapy, and pool therapy. I had great insurance, but it eventually ran out. The day my therapists told me there was no more they could do for me, I asked my son — who knew Anson from the gym — to set up an appointment for me to meet Anson.

When I rolled into the gym's front door in my wheelchair, Anson was there to greet me.

"You're not bringing that wheelchair in here," Anson said.

I was a little shocked and wondered what I was going to do. But Anson assured me he would do his best to get me walking again. Thanks to my mother-in-law, I was able to afford joining the gym and workout with Anson because I would not have been able to do it on my own.

During my first workout, Anson wanted me to ride a stationary bike for 15 minutes. The problem is the cardio equipment is up two flights of stairs.

"Not a problem," Anson said. He literally bent over and lifted me onto his back and carried me up the stairs and put me on a bike. From then, I knew he was as determined as I was to get me back on my feet. "But I'm not going to do this forever. One of these days, you'll be walking up these stairs," he said.

He introduced me to The Walker Lifestyle right away. Anson told me, "I want you to use that walker every day, everywhere you go and that will be your therapy when you're not here in the gym." So it's about incorporating exercise into your life. The next thing we did was start building up my upper body strength. You'd think we'd focus on the legs, but he knew I needed arm strength to get myself in and out of the car, out of bed, out of the tub and to steady myself with the walker. For example, I can put gas in my car now by myself. All this helped me function instead of having to rely on my wife every time I had to sit down or get up.

Anson's got a huge heart. He has brought me so far because he's not only helped with my physical workouts, but with the mental workout too. His faith is encouraging. He tells me just about every day, "You're this close to walking." I know he knows because he's been there too, after breaking his back and having reconstructive knee surgery. He knows what it takes to overcome these challenges.

Some days other guys in the gym say to me, "Is Anson punishing you, or what?" That's because he'll put my walker way down at the end of the line of machines. But that's not punishment. That's because today

I can get up from each machine and step to the next one and the next and the next until I'm done. That's amazing progress for me!

Maybe the best part is we have a good time while we're doing it. Anson will tell me what's going on in his life, and I'll tell him what's going on in mine. Next thing you know, my 45-minute workout is up, and I'm thinking, "Where did all the time go?"

Anson truly is a different kind of person. He's a no frills kind of guy, and he seems to know exactly what I need each day. When I first started working with him, I couldn't lift my legs and was doing about 25 lbs. on the leg press machine. Now I'm up to 118 lbs.

He fires me up and always keeps things positive. He can tell when I'm getting down. Then he has a fun way, or a story to tell, that will put things back into perspective and get me moving again. Something's changed over the last year. Now there are guys in the gym who come up to me and say, "You are the inspiration to get my lazy butt out of bed and get into the gym."

It started with Anson. He never stopped believing that I will walk again. I believe it too. We're this close. Then I'll tackle those stairs.

From Fat to Fit

by Wendy Smith Montgomery

- *Age: 39*
- *Weight: 325 lbs., down to 155 lbs.*
- *Resides in: Sumrall, Mississippi*
- *Occupation: Personal Trainer / Childcare Provider / Nutritionist*
- *How long with Anson: 8 years*
- *Snapshot: Wendy is a mom to three children and let her health go for*

many years. She tried all kinds of ways to lose weight except for physical fitness. She's my "biggest loser," having lost a "whole person" worth of weight. Today, she is also a certified personal trainer.

I was miserable. I didn't like who I was. I didn't like the way I looked or the way I felt, and my health went downhill from there. Since seventh grade, I had weighed over 200 pounds, and after having three children, I packed on more weight. At my heaviest, the scale read 325 pounds.

Along the way, I tried every diet gimmick and quick fix I could find. The funniest one was I had heard you could curb your appetite by getting your ears stapled at certain pressure points. That didn't work, obviously.

I woke up one Sunday morning and it just hit me. I want to do something about this once and for all. I'd never stepped foot in a gym before. I dreaded the idea, but it was the only thing that I hadn't tried. So I decided to drive over to a gym I knew about. Once I got there, I sat in the parking lot for about thirty minutes. I wanted to throw up because I was so scared. Finally, I got out of the car and walked in.

When I entered, Anson was sitting behind the desk. I figured after one look at me, he was probably thinking, "This lady is crazy." But I looked at him and said, "I'm tired of being this big and this unhealthy and this tired all the time. But I don't know what to do, and I don't know how to do it. So I need somebody to help me."

"We can work with that," he said. "I'd be happy to work with you and happy to help you."

With that, I started my journey. Anson held my hand every step of the way. I didn't have a lot of faith in myself because everything I had tried failed. But Anson kept reassuring me, "Have faith in me, and I promise you, if you just do what I say and trust the process, it will happen. You just have to show up, and I'll do the rest."

We started out with baby weights, like three pound dumbbells for the shoulder press, and went from there. We focused on physical training, but he also gave me nutritional pointers like, "Eat lean and green," and "The less legs the better."

I was willing to do the work if Anson would tell me what to do. So for the first time in my life, I started to see results. I lost forty pounds in ninety days. Seeing the scale drop every month really helped me stay on course. But if I'm being real honest, it was Anson who kept me coming back. He was so motivating and encouraging. He wasn't afraid to put me on the spot too. If I was running late, he'd text me, "Hey, where are you at? You know, I'm here, what time are you going to be here? I'm waiting for you." If somebody is waiting on me or if I know that they're expecting me to be there, I'm not going to let them down. I felt like Anson was an answer to prayer because that's exactly what I needed to make this whole journey a success.

One day, Anson decided I was going to run a mile around a track. I told him, "No, I've never run a mile in my life." We had done sprints before, but never a full mile.

"Well, today you're going to start," he said. "Okay, let's go." And he ran the mile with me! That gives you an idea of what kind of man he is, and how he helped me.

Throughout that year, and since then, Anson always cheers for me. He always celebrated every little gain. It always seemed like seeing me succeed made him happy. It was never like a job for him. He wanted me to succeed as much as I wanted to. That's who he is. He takes it personal and he makes it his mission — to help you be your best.

After one year, I stepped on the scale at the gym. I couldn't help but start crying. It read 198 pounds, which was the first time since seventh grade I'd been under 200 pounds. Anson was on the side and noticed what was happening. He came over. "What happened? It's not that bad. Is it?"

I explained what it truly meant. I had lost 125 pounds in one year. Of course, then Anson teared up like a girl.

Since then, my body type has changed. I've replaced a lot of fat with muscle. About two years ago, I decided to become a certified personal trainer through the National Academy of Sports Medicine (NASM). Now I've replaced those baby weights with the shoulder press to 45-lb. dumbbells in each hand.

Now I feel like a new person. Heck, I lost (the equivalent of) one whole person. When you see and feel that kind of change, then it's addictive. I'm never going to stop.

I've always told Anson, "You know, my success would not be anywhere what it is now without you." So I give him at least half the credit. I did the other half.

Answering Prayers

by Shelia Spann, Pharm.D, CDE

- *Age: 59*
- *Weight: 208 lbs., down to 123 lbs.*
- *Resides in: Madison, Mississippi*
- *Occupation: Pharmacist / Health Coach for Diabetes Patients*
- *How long with Anson: 3 years*
- *Snapshot: Shelia survived Lupus and a kidney transplant but found herself weighing 208 pounds and barely able to walk. She lost her husband to a massive heart attack and was raising two children. She had tried to lose weight and even worked with other personal trainers, but nothing worked. Today, she is 123 pounds and has become a competitive golfer, training to represent the state of Mississippi in the next Donate*

Life Transplant Games in San Diego, July-August, 2022.

I remember seeing his picture hanging outside of a gym and wondered if Anson might be the answer to prayer that I had been seeking. I am a kidney transplant recipient as a result of Lupus and never was any good at getting physically fit. So I reached out to him. What caught my attention right away was his attitude and enthusiasm. But when I met him, I was scared. He was this big, good-looking, well-built man, and I didn't think someone like that would be able to help somebody like me.

During that first day, I could tell he was not just another trainer because he was treating me like I was not just another person. I could barely walk at the time and didn't have much self-esteem. But he said, "Now don't you worry about all that. Just get here." Those first few months were tough because I had to go in there (the gym) and sort of put on blinders because I knew people were looking at me, and just focus on what Anson was telling me.

After three months, I lost six pounds. I saw other people going to him two or three times a week, so I said to myself, "Well, maybe I need to go another two or three times a week." I was still embarrassed, so I'd go to the gym early in the morning just to learn the machines that he was telling me to use. He was doing his job, now it was time for me to do mine.

One day, Anson was teaching me how to do lunges. I was off balance and really struggling. Anson didn't ridicule me. You know what he did? He just gave me a hug, and said, "We're going to work on this, and you're going to do this." That's what it's like working with Anson. He seems to know what each of us need. Little did I realize, but I needed those lunges for my golf game.

That was three years ago. Now, my life is completely different. I'm down to 123 pounds, and I'm not looking back. I started to learn how to play golf. I'm running, and I even went hunting with Anson. I would have never done those things before. It's just phenomenal.

That's why I'm still working with Anson. I'm addicted to fitness now. I'll never change. He's helped give me a whole new perspective about myself. I feel better about myself and love myself a lot. I'm better looking, and I feel younger now than I was in high school. My kidneys are looking good. My immune system numbers are great, and I've stopped having to take blood pressure medicine. Plus, I decided to help others with their fitness, so I became a Certified Diabetes Educator.

Turns out, Anson was an answer to my prayers.

Paralyzed but Not Permanently

by J. D. Mathis

- *Age: 66*
- *Weight: 165 lbs.*
- *Resides in: Ridgeland, Mississippi*
- *Occupation: Rice Broker*
- *How long with Anson: 2 years*
- *Snapshot: Due to a car accident, JD was paralyzed from the waist down in 2018. Doctors told him to accept his condition. He and his wife, Roseann, decided not to listen to their advice. This lovely couple amazed me with their work ethic and attitude, which are second to none. He started off in a wheelchair, moved to a walker, then to crutches, and is now walking with assistance.*

On June 2, 2017, I had a one-car accident. Thank the Lord nobody else was involved. All the airbags deployed, and the engine started steaming up on me so I thought, "This thing is going to catch fire and burn me up." So I went to move my leg to get out, but it wouldn't move. It's hard to believe, but I didn't feel any pain despite having a broken spinal cord.

Five days later, on my wedding anniversary to Roseann, I had surgery. When my doctors were finally ready to release me, they told me not to expect to walk again and just accept the fact that this is my new life and learn to adapt. I remember telling Roseann, "They don't know me too well, do they?"

I began the rehabilitation process going to physical therapy for over a year. I started in a wheelchair and gradually moved my way to a walker, but I was still unable to maintain any balance.

About that time, we moved down to Ridgeland, which is outside of Madison, Mississippi. My son-in-law is good friends with Anson, and he gave me a gift certificate for training with Anson at the gym. Roseann and I have been working with him two days a week ever since. When I first started, I could not stand on my own. It's been a long, slow process, but now I can stand on my own and even walk with some assistance. When I was in the hospital, I was in shock and wouldn't talk for a few weeks. It was sad. What I love about Anson is he knows that feeling, and he knows what it takes to get back on your feet.

For me, half of the work is physical, but the other half is just keeping your attitude positive. Not only does Anson have a talent for understanding what you need to improve your condition, but he is encouraging and genuinely wants to help. He's not there just to go through the motions. He knows how to get on your level. He's kind and makes you comfortable. He's emotionally supportive as well as physically and spiritually. He's helped me on all those levels.

I don't honestly know if we ever thought I'd be able to get this far. I couldn't have done it without Anson and Roseann. I know other rice farmers who have had accidents and never made it out of the wheelchair. Well, they didn't have Anson, and they didn't have Roseann. Funny thing happened despite all this. Roseann says, "This is the best season of my life."

9

Ready For Love

S omething amazing happened when I got my priorities straight and my mental, emotional, physical, and spiritual health in order. I was able to see clearly what's important to me, who I am and want to be — and what kind of woman I want to share my life with.

Growing up early on, I saw how *not* to treat a woman. Beyond that, my mom wasn't around much after the second divorce, so I didn't get to learn much about women. My dad thought of women as second-class citizens. He would crack sexist jokes all the time. Along with experiencing the sexual abuse as a kid, I was out on a limb when it comes to love.

Through my young adulthood, I treated women like objects. Then, as I spent time in jail and the Navy, there was no room for women in my life. I was a late bloomer. Now don't get me wrong, I chased women around. I may have known about love, but I never knew true love. That may sound sad, but I believe God was preparing the best possible person in the world for me.

When I'm at the gym, there's no place for chatting-up women. I'm a professional and work with women all the time. I don't want to become that scumbag trainer who hits on everything that moves. I care about my reputation. I train a bunch of my friend's wives. I have never ever been with a married woman. It is wrong and it is career suicide in my profession.

But I have to admit I broke my own rule when Tiffany came walking through those gym doors. I'll never forget seeing her for the first time. Of course, she caught my eye because she's gorgeous. But I figured she was married, so I kept my distance.

Three or four months later, she connected with me on Facebook asking about training. I replied saying something like, "Well, check with your husband, and let me know if you want my help."

"I'm not married."

I told myself, "Yet."

A few days later, she came into the gym and I didn't waste any time inviting her to dinner that night. That was the start of something magical. About three dates later, we knew true love was on the horizon for us.

We both grew up in Mississippi but had our lives take us elsewhere in our twenties and thirties. I was in Oceanside, while she was in Vegas. But we both came back because we love it here. Tiffany is a graduate of the University of Mississippi School of Nursing, and we're both Ole Miss fans, and we share a passion for health and wellness. She's a nurse, so we're on the same page there. I love her character. She's selfless and honors her mom and stepdad by taking care of them and keeping a full-time job helping recovering addicts. She's a giver.

We've also both known pain. Her daddy left when she was three years old. She's had relationships that caused a lot of hurt. Thankfully, they made her a little gun-shy about trying again.

Thank God she did. In the last two years, we've really grown together. Tiffany was there for me when my dad died, which was a difficult time for me. We've also grown spiritually, following Christ the best we can.

126

‌‌‌‌

It's been amazing. I wish I could explain what it's like to be loved as much as I love her. We're both on the same team, and everybody else is a distant third. I'm at a whole new level in life because of Tiffany. It's a totally different program when you experience love at such a deep level. It changes everything.

That's why a few months back, and behind Tiffany's back, I went over to visit her parents and asked their permission to marry their daughter. I bought a ring and started planning a proposal. Thanks to COVID, I had delays with the ring. But soon enough, the stage was set.

We went to our favorite restaurant — Two Rivers in Canton, Mississippi. Beforehand, I dropped off two dozen roses for them to arrange on a tray. When the waitress came over to serve our "appetizer," the ring was right in the middle of these roses. I took the ring out of the box, looked at Tiffany, and dropped out of my chair on my knee.

"Will you marry me?" The biggest question of my life came out of my mouth, as all the guests in the restaurant watched. She was blown away.

"Yes, I will."

Everyone started applauding us. We both smiled and laughed so hard our cheeks were hurting. It was the most important moment of my life. And I know it's forever. Besides, despite my parent's marital problems, my dad taught me, "If you start something, you can't quit. Always finish what you start."

> *If you start something, you can't quit.*
> *Always finish what you start.*
> *— Dan Walker Rule*

To think about all I've been through, and to end up engaged to the most incredible woman I've ever known is just a miracle. It really is. I've transformed from a Geico caveman into a Southern gentleman with true responsibility. My job now is to provide for and protect my fiance. And I look forward to that awesome responsibility.

The Walker Lifestyle has prepared me for this. I've grown in my character, learned what matters, and persevered through so many tough times. I'm healthy as a horse, and now I'm able to give all of myself to Tiffany. I'm still a work in progress, and always will be. In fact, I'm still in elementary school when it comes to love. But I look forward to being the best I can be in that category too — which officially begins on June 25, 2022.

Letter from Tiffany

To Anson — my love, my heart, my best friend:

When I first wake up, I can barely form complete sentences. "Thirsty, gotta pee, tired," is all I can really say out loud. But when I wake up, I see a man who is so energetic and full of life! From the minute he opens his eyes, he makes me laugh saying things like, "Good morning you beautiful bitch!" Who says that? Who is that full of life and happy so quickly after they wake up!?" We start the mornings with laughter and love every day.

The first time I laid eyes on Anson was at Starke Fitness. I had just bought my first home and was looking for a gym. Fitness has always been incredibly important to me. Although competing in figure competitions is no longer something I want to pursue, it has instilled in me what a person can accomplish with their bodies through consistency and perseverance at a gym. As I was on the stair stepper one early morning around 5:00 a.m. at my new gym, I saw this guy running his bootcamp with girls running up and down the stairs with weights. He showed no mercy and was loud! I was on the stepper and thought, "Who does this guy think he is being so loud and aggressive?" But I also thought, "Damn, he's gorgeous." (Years later, those two young women, Beth and Annette, are still in his bootcamp and look phenomenal).

Time marched on and ultimately, he friended me on Facebook. Yet he never said a thing to me at the gym. I will never forget the moment I started falling for him. It was a July 4th weekend on a Sunday, and I was at the gym on the stepper. I could see this guy on a nearby StairMaster, sweating in a weight vest and absolutely killing it. Most guys are glued to the TV on Sunday, but not Anson. I watched him leave, noticing he's got that walk . . . that football player, athletic, confident walk. Women know what I mean. Men who are active and athletic have a certain posture, composure, stance. It's the way they carry themselves that is very attractive.

After that, I decided to reach out on Facebook to ask him for training. Yes, he still teases me to this day that I reached out to him first! To this day, I don't regret it! I asked him to train me, even though I know damn well what to do. Instead of training me, by the end of the week, we had our first date.

On the first date, I answered my door to this gorgeous man holding a dozen red roses. Since then, rarely have I ever answered my door on a date night that he wasn't standing there holding a dozen red roses. And never have I been anywhere with him that he didn't open his vehicle door for me. That night, he took me to Two Rivers, a restaurant in Canton, Mississippi, I had never been to before. We had an amazing night with awesome food and atmosphere. Anson surprisingly told me everything about his life . . . everything including his time in jail. I found his honesty refreshing! I didn't have to wonder who he was. He was so sincere and just laid it all out, like here it is. Take it or leave it, this is me. So I blurted out, "I can't have children and you don't have any so . . . I know you want them." He laughed, grabbed *my hand and said, "No ma'am, I've got two nieces. I'm good."*

This began our beautiful, sweet, passionate love affair. The sunrises I have experienced with this man have been incredible — deep sea fishing in Venice, Louisiana, watching the sun rise while fishing in Gulf Shores. All of these things I had never experienced before. Anson loves life, and he taught me to get out of my comfort zone and live these beautiful outdoor experiences with him. I wouldn't take anything for those memories.

Are we perfect? No. Is our relationship perfect? No. Do we fight? Lord Jesus yes! I want to be as real, raw, and transparent as I know Anson is. That is the reason why people love him. So here are just a few fights to keep it real:

The Missing Black Socks

Anson's Dad, aka Big D, passed away. It was the morning of Big D's funeral. I had cleaned Anson's house the night before and thought we were good and prepared for the people who might stop by after the funeral. But when I arrived the next morning, it looked like a murder scene. Anson was bloody because his nose bleeds when he is super stressed out. He was up most of the night preparing his Dad's eulogy. I rolled up my "church dress" sleeves and took my heels off to clean up. Anson was so incredibly sad and stressed out. I mean who wouldn't be with the death of their father? Even though he is a public speaker at many events, it's different when it's your parent. He wore a black suit, but we couldn't find black socks anywhere in the house. Time was going by fast and anybody who knows Anson knows he is never late. At one point, he took his sock drawer out of the dresser and threw it across the room. We argued, apologized, and eventually, after I found the socks, laughed in his father's name. We were still the first ones to arrive at the funeral home. Anson and his brother, Matt, both gave amazingly beautiful speeches. I know Big D was proud!

The Funeral Procession Flashers

Anson was one week post op from knee surgery and could not drive to his father's burial site after the funeral. The funeral director lined us up, placing Anson as the firstborn, the first in line behind the hearse. I know he struggled with not being able to drive to his father's gravesite, so I drove him. As we headed down Hwy 51, I noticed his brother behind me had his flashers on, which reminded me to turn on our flashers. Everything was going fine, until we both tried to find the right button for the flashers. There were so many buttons in my new car. We both started pushing all these buttons. Anson accidentally pushed the button that turns my car off. I slammed on the brakes and came within inches of slamming into Big D in the hearse. The entire funeral procession almost did the same behind us.

So there was a mini fight and awkward silence for a while. I know Big D is still laughing!

My point is that we are not perfect by any means, but I love Anson B. Walker with all my heart!

If Sumrall Farms cornfield could speak of the passionate love we have for each other, y'all wouldn't even watch the TV series Yellowstone.

I love You Anson,
  Tiffany

10

The Best Me

I'm not where I want to be. But I'm also not where I was. And that is progress considering I started out abused and confused, later being incarcerated then broken physically, mentally, emotionally, and spiritually. I'm proud of myself for where I am today. But that's not the end of the story. The best is yet to come.

I believe people do not decide their futures. Instead, they decide their habits and their habits decide their futures. I'm proud of my habits and am eager to see where they lead me.

I've learned a lot about myself and human nature over the course of my time here on God's great earth. Looking back, I realized I had a lot of selfish habits, which, quite frankly, are embarrassing. Back when I was contaminated with selfishness and greed, I chased women, money, and alcohol, which became habits that would determine my future. I am not proud of it, but it happened. What do you do? Act like it didn't happen? Because it did. (To whom it may concern: I am deeply sorry if I hurt you, male or female. I was lost, sick, and carrying a lot of guilt at the time. I am very sorry for everything wrong that I have done.) I paid dearly for those bad habits, including money with 6 percent interest, guilt, embarrassment, and lost friendships. I still have nightmares about prison, judges, trials, and being in an orange jumpsuit and lying to my mom, "I didn't do it."

I think it's God's way of reminding me to stay on the right path, to stay humble, to remain honest, dedicated, and committed to what's right. I promised my mom years ago that if I got a second chance in life I would take advantage of it. I think if you asked my mom right now if she's proud of her oldest son you would get a resounding "YES!"

I have learned from my mistakes. They changed me, molded me, gave me purpose and appreciation for life like I've never known before. I have the bruises, scars, and the collateral damage to prove it. The military instilled some awesome discipline and accountability and structure that I needed at that time in my life. Then I took it to another level on my own. But you gotta understand. Anson Walker loves a good scar. You can learn from it, change from it, and use it to teach others. I don't recommend taking the path I took to get to your stage of enlightenment in your life, but I sure hope you can use my mistakes, my life lessons, and apply them for your benefit. That is what I want.

The Walker Lifestyle was born out of my former life. The Walker Lifestyle is nothing more than a series of habits and mindsets that, if used correctly, can help you in every phase of your life. These fundamental principles apply to the playing field, classroom, from the boardroom to the bedroom, and everywhere in between. There are no side effects, except feeling better, being stronger, and having more energy.

What do I want? I want my clients, friends, family, and followers to win in every area of their life. In fact I insist on it. Being healthy, mentally and physically, exudes over to other areas of your life. When a married couple tells me their relationship is better than ever, I feel joy and am proud of them because they are winning. The same goes for the CEO, the stay-at-home mom, those making a comeback from injury, and many others who decide to do something good for themselves. We all deserve a healthy body, mind, and soul. That's what we're given to work with, but now we have to do our part. Most people don't know their role or their part. That is where I come in.

By no means is The Walker Lifestyle the only way to do it, but it's what I know, and it's working. From the ESPN Radio show audience, to my clients, to my family, to my friends, the overwhelming following and support is amazing. I know it works because of the hundreds and hundreds of confirmations I receive each month.

_____

My (Your) 2022 Declarations

What are your New Year's resolutions? They may sound something like this:

- *I'm going to quit smoking on January 1st.*
- *No more alcohol for me.*
- *I'm going to eat healthy and exercise — gym time every day.*
- *I'm going to stop dating toxic people.*
- *No more social media.*
- *No more gambling baby. That's the last $500 I will ever lose.*
- *I'm going to read my Bible every day.*

Whatever your resolutions were last year, how did they go? I would venture to say some probably went well, while others, maybe not. Typically, we will fall off the wagon, feel the guilt and misery of looking at these resolutions and realizing we quit before we even got started. Then we're back to square one. Why does this happen?

Behavior modification doesn't work because the focus is only on modifying the behavior. This doesn't get to the root of the problem, which is the thought that produces the behavior.

If you think you can change behavior by making a resolution, you're swimming upstream. It's almost impossible. The behavior isn't the problem. The problem is your habits that lead to the behavior. The behavior will not come back unless you change your habits 100 percent. Here's an example: A rut is typically formed in mud and becomes a nuisance, even a danger. A rut is unintentionally created. It has no purpose and requires repair. A trench is intentionally dug to deliver a necessary resource. A trench has a specific purpose and fixes an existing problem. Friends, we all know that the only antidote for a lie is truth, for darkness its light, for wrong, there is right, from guilt to forgiveness, from selfish to selfless, from hate to love.

There is a solution. You can fix yourself. I've done it. I believe in making specific declarations, not resolutions. For example, one powerful declaration is, "I will create winning habits."

I have hundreds of clients over the years who have fixed themselves too. How? Through The Walker Lifestyle, a series of habits that eventually become a way of life. I actually don't even think about it now, because the decision was made over fifteen years ago. Instead of living in a rut, you can create a truth trench that runs deeper, diverting the flow of your thoughts from old pathways to new ones. We each have a series of set thoughts that we think each time we are triggered. For you, the trigger may be feeling alone, fear of failure, or being around people who are smoking or drinking. The point is that you fall into the same series of thoughts you always fall into, and they lead to the same behavior. What each of us has to do is this: we have to strategically chase a new series of thoughts, which lead to a new series of habits, winning habits.

Where do we get these new thoughts? Hint, not social media. Not that toxic friend. Me? Well, I try to start with God's Word. Remember that's the weapon God gives us for the battle we are fighting. His truth is what sets us free. That's what Jesus did. He used the scripture to apply directly to temptations he faced. When Satan tempted him, Jesus couldn't whip out his iPhone and open up his YouVersion Bible app to search for a verse that might help. He had already internalized truth from God's Word that created a helpful habit. When tempted, Jesus followed the path that led him to obedience and freedom. That's what we've gotta do folks. I deal with a lot of negatives and a lot of distractions in my line of work. And y'all, here's how I handle 'em. Number one, mindset. I have to think differently.

"Well Anson, I'm gonna try."

Wrong. That's a loser mindset. There is no try. There is do and there is don't do. There is no try. Let's try that again.

"Anson, I'm gonna do it." That's a winner-mindset attitude. You control this 100 percent of the time. It's getting what you get and not pitching a fit. Friends, act with a purpose. Effort. You control this 100 percent of the time. Effort has to do with how hard you're trying. Effort teaches us we can do more than we thought, always.

Reacting to other people's fits, I say, grow the hell up. You control how you respond to other people. Period.

Regarding food: Follow these simple habits and you'll win. Remember my 80–20 rule? Eat clean, and for those of you over 40, think 90–10, eating clean 90 percent of the time. Remember that grilled is better than fried; the less legs the better — hence fish is the best, chicken is the second best, etc. This isn't kindergarten. We don't need treats for normal behavior. You need to eat clean. You need clean calories.

Regarding prescription pills: In many cases, I think a healthy goal is to try to get off of prescription medicine. If you're 20–30 pounds overweight and your doctor hasn't recommended sunshine, vitamin D, eating clean, and getting some exercise then you may want to change doctors.

Alcohol: It's the single worst calorie intake on planet earth. The only thing alcohol does well is get you drunk. Period. Abuse of this product is insane. You want to change your body and mind? Stop abusing alcohol.

Negative people: I've discussed this many times in my radio segments in the past. There's absolutely no room in my life for negative or toxic people.

Zero tolerance. Friends, this goes for what we feed our minds too. There is so much negativity online, on our TV shows, even commercials that want you to think you need their products, are all appalling at best.

Remember the line "You are what you eat?" Same goes for what you watch. Avoid toxic input from porn, online gambling, and overly violent shows. You are the company you keep, which includes your daily entertainment.

My 2022 declaration? We are all different, and I thank God for that. My declaration for this year is: free to be me. You cannot give what you do not have. I choose to give hope, optimism, love, patience, second chances, empathy, knowledge, etc. to my people, my clients, my friends, my fiance. Why? Because it's been given to me by different individuals over my life. In all the world, there's not one exactly like me. Everything that comes out of me is authentically mine because I choose it. I own it. I own everything about me, my body, my mind, my feelings, my language — which is not good sometimes — my voice, all my actions, whether they be to others or to myself.

I own my dreams, my hopes, my fears. I own my mistakes, my failures, my shortcomings, because I'm far from perfect. And that's all on me, period. Any successes I enjoy are for Tiffany and myself. That credit goes to God, because I am His, period. I honor God, period. I glorify God, period. You don't know my internal makeup, my bruises, my scars, the hurt, the pain, the setbacks, the abuse I've had to endure. God does. And he allowed it, because I can handle it and use it to help others avoid it. And guess what? I earned those bruises, cuts, scars, and I'm proud of every one of them. I have become intimately acquainted with myself. What I mean by that is I have stared down my demons.

It took me a long time to love myself. I know there are aspects about myself that puzzle me and other aspects that I do not know. But as long as I am friendly and loving to myself, I can courageously and hopefully look for solutions to the questions, to the puzzles that need to be solved mentally. I'm still learning about life daily. That's why I read. I'm still learning about myself daily. I have a hunger for information concerning God, the Son, and the Holy Spirit, and that thirst can only be quenched by God.

However, I look around at whatever I say and do, and whatever I see and feel at any given moment is authentically me. I'm very comfortable as to where I am, what I stand for, and my purpose for my short time here on earth. I am in tune with my senses better than ever before. I see, hear, feel, touch, taste, think, speak, and do so with a spiritual, mental, and physical awareness like I've never had before. I'm sure being 100 percent in love with my fiance, Tiffany, has something to do with that. But I can tell you this: I don't know all the answers I seek. I have the mental and physical tools to survive any circumstances, period. I also have the tools to be close to others, to be productive, to win, to make sense and order out of this world of people and things outside of me. I own me. I control myself. Therefore, I engineer myself.

I'm here in 2022 to win and to win big. I want you to join me in The Walker Lifestyle and win in every area of your life. For you to win, you must change your habits. You must change you. No one owes you anything. If you need to increase your business, do it now. If you need to have an honest talk with your spouse, define a few things, do it now. If your kids are disrespectful, fix it. If you don't, you're only setting them up for failure in life. Say you don't have enough time in the day? Get your ass up at 4:00 a.m. It works. You'll go to bed earlier. You'll get more done.

Lastly, I try to be transparent at everything I do. My Facebook posts, my Instagram posts, my radio segments are all aimed to help you win. I promise. I can help too. It's what I do. I only have around 500 personal character references, so please feel free to ask any one of them. Please join my family, whether it's here at Starke Fitness or online, and let's make 2022 the year you made a change forever.

What's Next for Me?

I love to encourage people. I love to see them win. I have a voice, a proven method, and a passion that aligns with others' goals to be well. So I plan to keep on keeping on, broaden my horizons, and increase my platforms so I can help more people.

This includes targeting the state of Mississippi, the fattest state in the U.S. If I can reduce the obesity rate by just 1 percent, it will impact 30,000 people. My company, Walker Lifestyle Consulting, will set out to reach both the young, old, 9 to 5 work crew, business owners and the overweight, out-of-shape, or broken adults. Since they will not all be able to visit me at Starke Fitness and Wellness, I'm building an online platform where y'all can tap into The Walker Lifestyle from your computer keyboards or mobile devices. I will also be able to refer you to products like BCAA's, creatine, and isolate protein powders that I use. I'm going to provide video instruction and motivation for members of my online world.

It will start with my 7-Day Reboot Bootcamp that can be done either at home or at the gym, and it includes a little education so we learn about how and why we need to reboot fitness in our lives. These practical movements start the process of building consistency without an excuse. Everyone can do these exercises, and my job is to help you actually do them! These boot camps will be done in-person and online, with corporations seeking to improve their employee's health, and others, whether we meet in a park, gym, parking lot, or a living room.

The bottom line is I'll never stop trying to be the best me, and that includes helping you become the best you.

Walker Lifestyle Consulting will focus on building the bridge between employees and their upline–no matter how far that goes. Managers have to be able to effectively communicate to the employees what ownership needs, and ultimately comprehend and explain the vision of the company. The "Team" applies to many things we do here on earth and it is certainly not limited to sports. Military and gym teams are more important to me than the championship varsity college football and baseball teams I was a part of. Why? Because my military and gym teams directly affected spouses, children, clients, members, the community, and more.

For CEOs, Human Resource Directors, middle managers and everyone from the mailroom to the board room, here are 10 reasons to choose Walker Lifestyle Consulting.

1. Great consultants are flexible.

Great consultants adapt to new projects, work cultures and colleagues easily. They come in, they fit in and they get the job done. Their soft skills and technical expertise allow them to take on their roles quickly and easily. There are 24 hours in a day. I know we can fit in one or two to make your company successful.

2. Great consultants have great discipline.

Great consultants work hard and they work smart. They know how to accomplish the best results in the shortest possible time with as little friction as possible. It takes discipline, and sometimes that means great consultants have to be great problem solvers too. I have always said "Discipline gives you freedom." It's so true. Once you grasp that concept you can literally increase your effectiveness in everything you do by 200 percent. That is not a lofty aspiration. It is a fact.

3. Great consultants are confident.

Let's not confuse this with arrogance. Arrogance is one of my pet peeves and it has zero effectiveness. If you think you know everything you can't be coached, you can't learn and grow as a person, as a leader, as a winner. The most successful people I know, learn from, collaborate with weekly are still reading, learning, applying, and teaching everyday.

They are getting better daily! Great consultants are confident about their skills and expertise. They expose natural collaborative leadership and they leave their egos at the door. Great consultants are team players. They put company goals and team spirit first. I know this from personal experience. If I can help my clients get what they want, I will get what I want. It's a mathematical equation that works every time. I am confident, but I'll leave my ego at the door. If you do the same, you will win big.

4. Great consultants are persistent.

I control two things in my life. My attitude and my effort–100 percent of the time. My secret power is my resilience to bounce back after falling flat, and persistence that never gives up. They accept friction, unforeseen circumstances and negative feedback, they learn from them and they move on. I can't control people but I can control how I react to people. I teach my clients how to do that. They will analyze and learn from every setback in order to prevent it from happening again. Mistakes are a good thing, not a bad thing as long as we learn from them.

5. Great consultants are studious.

The key to being a great wellness consultant is to be studious. How? Listen. WE have two ears and one mouth for a reason. We need to use them in that ratio. If you will actually practice listening instead of talking, you will learn 100 percent more every day. I know this because I learned the hard way. When I didn't have anyone to talk to, I learned to listen — by reading from the greatest authors in the world. What are you reading? Who are you listening to? What are you learning? What are you applying in your life daily? What are you teaching? Understanding these gifts are a must for training others! Great consultants never stop learning. They need to stay on top of the developments in their fields of expertise. It is their job to bring the latest knowledge and skills to the table when others can't. I can't control anything else but me, my rate of learning, and my effectiveness to my clients.

6. Great consultants are like MacGyver.

Remember MacGyver, the hero of the popular 80's TV show? He could solve any problem with his mind and his Swiss army knife. The same goes for great consultants; they use skills and knowledge from previous projects to solve new problems and challenges. I thank God for the obstacles and the problems in my life because it gave me a passion and a purpose, as well as prepared me for the work ahead. Each challenge is unique and offers new opportunities to brainstorm and utilize my resources to accomplish the goals. My job is to fix/improve things and watching the transformation is my reward!

7. Great consultants go further.

Great consultants see the big picture and the small parts that can make it better. Consultants bring a fresh view, offer surprising insights and are willing to go the extra mile which can solve problems and boost the client's business. My life's experience has developed in me a diverse set of skills. I have been around the world. I have been involved with fortune 500 companies and I have been in jail. I have served this country in the United States Navy and personally trained over 3,300 clients thus far. I'll never claim to know it all but I like my chances in helping because of my experience, perspective and willingness to work harder than the other guy. I actually like telling people, "I don't know......but I will find out.......and that is a promise!"

8. Great consultants don't assume.

The reason I don't assume anything is this universal law—inevitably I'll make an "ass" out of "u" and "me." Hence the word "assume." I take this seriously because I'm willing to admit I don't know something in order to learn something. It's a great exchange that leads to progress.

9. Great consultants are sociable.

I am not referring to the country club socialite here. I truly believe there is a relationship to be built with everyone. I am passionate when I say this, "Life is about building relationships!" Why else are we here? I love people and I love helping people reach their potential. Most people do not realize the talents God has blessed them with until they are brought into an environment or person that brings it out of them. I try to become that person!

And last but not least:

10. Great consultants ask questions.

Great consultants ask great questions. It's vital to seek to understand before trying to be understood. I will know next to nothing about you or your company's situation. So, I have to ask the right questions so I can process the information. There is no time limit in this step of the process. My primary goal is to help other people and businesses, not me. I know about me. I need to know about you. So, I must be able to inquire so that I can inspire. Besides, without asking questions, trust will never take root. Great consultants build trust because of their will to understand their clients and related needs so they can accomplish their goals. It's really simple.

Closing Anson-isms

- It's okay to fail. It's okay to make mistakes. It's okay to be tired. It's okay to hurt. It's okay to cry. It's okay to love. But it's not okay to quit! Never ever, ever.
- Be relationship-oriented before goal-oriented. Then both will happen.
- Reality is a dream that is focused on my reality. It's not based on anyone's opinion, no matter who they are. It lies in my experience

and my vision.

- My faith is in God, in me, and my abilities to focus on my dreams. By putting life in this priority order, my dreams will become realities.
- You've got to go into that deep ocean. That's where the big treasure is found.
- "It" won't work for others but if you work, you dream, you imagine, you work some more, whatever your "it" is will work for you!
- No one has your gifts. That's why they can't see what you can see. The same applies to me.
- It takes just one idea for you to change the course of history for you forever. Then get ready to friggin' work your ass off to make it a reality. Actions beat intentions every time.
- It's only crazy to everyone else, whatever "it" is! The best part is that each of our "its" are different.
- To positively influence people is the best way to live. Long after I have lived, I want to be known as someone who affected others, touched them, and convinced them to believe in themselves. It's magical when others grasp onto what I am teaching, whether it benefits their physical, mental, emotional or spiritual condition. It takes faith, passion, and conviction. But if I'm telling you I believe it, you can bet your life on it.

The bottom line is I'll never stop trying to be the best me, and that includes helping you become the best you.

11

The Best You

I f you have made it this far in the book, that tells me a few things about you:

1. You want to learn.
2. You want to get better.
3. You want to win in life.
4. You care about your health (mental and physical).
5. You L.O.V.E. (Let's Overcome Various Entities).

I'm proud of you. You've invested the price of this book and the time to come alongside me on my journey, and I trust you have seen or heard something you like. But this book is not really about me. You see, my greatest desire is to help you become the best you.

Now I'm about to help you give yourself the greatest return on investment in the history of the world! Let's finish strong. Let's win this thing together! So here it goes. I have experienced a lot in my forty-seven years, like:

- I went through extreme childhood abuse.
- I experienced extreme emotional/mental abuse at times by my

father.

- I have been bullied and picked on.
- I broke the law, which led to jail time.
- Life dealt me a broken back, broken ribs, broken tailbone, and broken mind, body, and soul!

Is it fair?

Heck no. Does anyone else besides my family really care? No. Why? It's no one else's life. It's mine. Period.

Is it personal?

No. It's just life, friends, and we are all trying to get through it the best we can. But through it all, God has always been there whether or not I reached out. I wavered, but God never did. I lied, cheated, and stole. But God's grace was enough. I broke promises, but God keeps his promises.

In life, people will hurt you, lie to you, steal from you. They will disappoint you — not all, but some will, and it's often the ones you least expect. Guess what? It will never change. Hence, that is life, friends. However, you are bigger and better than all that! All of that stops today. Why? Because you control three things 24/7 and forever:

1. Your attitude.
2. Your effort.
3. How you react to difficult people and circumstances.

Whether you think you can't or you think you can, you're right! Immaturity is for the birds. Grow up Peter Pan. Let's win the day, the week, the month, and this year! *You* control it, and nobody else does. Your faith in the truth will set you free. A winning mindset and positivity are the keys. Winning thinking helped me find the love of my life. Winning thinking helps me help others daily. Winning thinking will help you too! You control this! There is never a perfect time to start, but it can also become too late. Knowing that, I want to impress this into your brain: Let's do it now! Not tomorrow. Now!

The Walker Lifestyle is nothing more than a refreshing and new way to view life, to instill positive habits that will have you winning in every area of your life. How do I know this? Because you are reading the book of a loser who got sick and tired of losing. I changed my thought process in every capacity. I changed my habits in every capacity. I was tired of who I was. I got my ass up off the ground one more time, and it has made all the difference in the world. I was a bona fide loser who became a winner. I got one more rep, tried one more time, hurt one more time, regretted one more time, and got fed up one more time with . . . me.

This did not happen overnight, over a week, or over a month. But I strung a few days together, which became a week, then a month. Then I won a year or two. Fast-forward, and now I have a platform to share what I've learned, which has been battle tested. I have the scars to prove it.

Along the way, I have reached thousands of people with my message of hope and encouragement. I've worked with hundreds personally, and have at least 500 people who will testify that my methods and approach to health and fitness has become their absolute gospel. I don't pretend to have all the answers, but using The Walker Lifestyle on a daily basis gives me a *chance* to win daily.

Do I win every day?

No. But am I in a position to win?

Yes, I am. Just when I may think I'm pushing a client too hard or maybe take a position that's questionable on a certain topic, I seek a confirmation from God that I am indeed doing the right thing, every time friends. Ultimately, I think that humility is the difference between winning and losing. Guess what? You are about to win and win big baby!

I can't stress this enough: My life changed 180 degrees when I decided enough was enough. When I decided to look at the man in the mirror and call myself out, I changed. I started working harder, smarter, more intensely, listening more and talking less, reading more books and Scripture than ever before. It helped get me out of a self-imposed rut and turned it into a truth trench with a purpose. If you don't know your purpose, it will come if you work on yourself daily. Eventually you will find your purpose. I promise.

Succeeding

Why is this time different for you? Because this time, you will take action and have my personal support every step of the way. I'm about to coach you online from here on out. You will have access to me 24/7 via email, via Facebook, Instagram, and Twitter. Beyond that, I'm inviting you to jump on my website and become a premium member of the Walker Lifestyle Training Group. Your monthly membership will include access to supplements, workouts, and guidance from me on a weekly basis. I'm planning to have guest speakers, success stories, instructional videos, my go-to books, my favorite Scripture verses, and a question portal. Nothing is off limits, just keep it PG-13.

Action

The next thirty days are critical. Get the premium Walker Lifestyle Subscription. Join a gym, and get to work! Tune in to my radio segment on ESPN Radio 105.9 FM Jackson, Mississippi, every Wednesday at 3:00 p.m. Central Standard Time (or get it https://www.thezone1059.com/the-zone-on-demand/). Plug in daily to my guidance. Learning never stops, for me included. It's 4:30 a.m. and I am writing this chapter after reading thirty pages from *Atomic Habits* by James Clear.

You have to make a conscious and intentional effort to win daily! It will not happen on its own. Winning and learning to win never stops. Remember, it is you vs. you. Don't be a knucklehead and try to compare yourself to me or anyone else. Instead, keep your eyes on the prize — the best you can be.

You will become a better version of you in daily, weekly, monthly, and annual increments. I know because I've been there. Making a comeback starts with starting. I want to be with you along the way. I don't leave teammates behind . . . ever.

Get your priorities lined up, and execute a plan. Giving up on yourself means giving up on your priorities and others. The point is you have to take care of yourself first before you can be the best you. I am "free to be the best me" because I intentionally work on my mental and physical health daily. It's a vital necessity that can't be ignored. I can't, so I won't stop.

Join my family forever by activating The Walker Lifestyle Premium Membership, and I will have your back forever! I love you, and I am proud of you. The time has come for you to win. The only thing stopping you is you. Remove the excuses and take action. Regardless if you join me or go alone, I'm excited about the new you. And you should be too! God doesn't make mistakes. He made you for a reason, and he has a purpose for you that's bigger than you can imagine. Now is the time to find out what that is. Let's GO!

Very respectfully yours,
  — Anson B. Walker

Appendix

The 7-Day Reboot Bootcamp

Sometimes in life, and fitness, you have to reboot the system, start over (again), switch things up, and get back on track. With the 7-Day Reboot Bootcamp, I've outlined a way for you to do just that with your fitness. The main goal of the bootcamp is to start, then stick with it, even if you have to modify the exercises to suit your condition, because you won't see physical changes in seven days. But with this one-week program, you can repeat it each week for a month, and I'll be shocked if you don't improve in your strength and conditioning and maybe even drop a belt loop.

If you're still hung up on fearing soreness or getting "bulky," I've added a bonus section after the bootcamp instructions that gives you my take on several of the most common myths about fitness.

Get These Instructions and More when you sign up at TheWalkerLifestyle.com!

I'll do my best to give you exercises that can be done at home with your own body weight. But I'd be pulling your leg if I told you that would be enough. That's why the first thing I suggest is to find a gym or health club nearby and invest in yourself. The gym will have equipment, weights, and group classes that give you far more options than you probably have in your living room or garage. Then hire one of the personal trainers and/or sign up for TheWalkerLifestyle.com membership online. This is critical because even the most experienced fitness experts know they need to execute the movements correctly to get the most benefit and avoid injury.

If you live in Mississippi, anywhere near Jackson, Madison, or Canton, then get down to Starke Fitness (109 Dees Drive, Madison) and you can work out with me.

Nutrition Guidelines

During the 7-Day Reboot Bootcamp, I want you to follow the nutritional Ground Rules outlined in the book, chapter 6. As a reminder, the primary principles are:

- **Eat lean and green.**
- **The less legs the better.**
- **Use carbs wisely.**
- **Follow the 80–20 rule.**

From there, I've outlined the following exercises to do for five days, giving you two days of rest in one week. You may want to use a journal during the first week to jot down the amount of weight you're using, and any tips about the execution you learn.

Exercise Guidelines

1. Unless otherwise stated, execute each exercise for 4 sets of 12 reps (aka 4x12).
2. If you're just starting out after a long layoff, use a low amount of

weights and focus on getting the right technique and "waking up" the muscles. Otherwise, find the amount of weight that will force you to push the last two reps with difficulty.

3. For at-home exercises that require weights or dumbbells, you can either buy some, use exercise bands, or create homemade alternatives. You can try:

4. Gallons for milk

5. Buckets filled with sand, dirt, or water

6. Firewood

7. Tools

8. Plastic bags filled with material

9. Recommend following days 1–5 for Monday-Friday, and use Saturday and Sunday to rest and recover, while adding some fun exercise (like golf, hunting, swimming, hiking, playing a sport, bike riding, etc.).

10. Day 5 is a "Wildcard" day, which means you can choose which exercise to train each muscle group, excluding the muscles used the previous day. In this case, exclude exercises targeting the back and triceps.

11. Sign up at **AnsonBWalker.com** to get a FREE 30-day trial for The Walker Lifestyle membership, and to watch the videos for each of the exercises below.

DAY 1 — Chest and Triceps

AT HOME

Push-ups (from your toes or knees depending on your strength)

- Push-up position includes keeping your back straight, hands located under your shoulders — or slightly wider than shoulder width. Lower yourself all the way to the ground and push up to a full extension of your arms. Be sure to get the full range of motion, and do not cheat by going only half way down or pushing up without fully extending your arms.

Plank (from push-up position or on forearms) — 6 sets, 30 seconds each

- Use the push-up position (or from forearms) and hold for 30 seconds. Then rest for 10 seconds. Keep back straight, with shoulders locked.

Cardio — 15–30 minutes (walk at fast pace, or bike)

- This is not a leisure stroll. Instead walk briskly with long strides. If on the bike, choose a route that includes some hills to climb. You may also choose to increase walking or biking speeds with intervals of slower paces.

AT GYM

Chest press

- Prefer using a machine. Settle into the machine to make sure you can get a full range of motion from the bar, or handles, that reach your chest to a full extension of the arms. Then avoid using your shoulders, or arching your back, to assist in the movement. Don't hold your breath. Instead exhale slowly on each push.

Tricep dumbbell kickbacks

- Use a bench to kneel on one knee. Bend forward so you can place your hand, from the same side as the kneeling knee, onto the bench. Use the other leg to balance the crouch position. Grab the dumbbell with the other hand. Lift straight up so your elbow is at a 45-degree angle. From there, press the dumbbell backward toward your rear (this is the "kickback"). In the full extension, your arm should be nearly straight and parallel to the ground, which completes one rep. Slowly bend your elbow back to the 90-degree position to start the second rep. Note: This can be done from the standing position. Just bend at the waist so your arms can be extended and parallel to the ground.

Dumbbell chest press

- Use dumbbells in both hands. Sit on a bench with weights on your knees. As you lean back onto the bench, pull and press the dumbbells into the upright position, directly over your shoulders. While lying flat on the bench, bring the dumbbells down to your chest with elbows pointing out. Press the dumbbells directly up for one rep. Avoid arching your back.

Tricep machine

- Adjust the arm levers so you can get a full extension. After selecting the weight, push the levers away from your shoulder until they are fully extended. Focus on using the tricep muscles only.

Core: Ab Ball series — Starting position is the same for each of the following exercises, with your lower back on the Ab Ball so your rear-end is barely touching.

- Crunch: With arms crossed in front of your chests, contract your lower and mid-abs to raise your shoulders and upper back off the ball for one rep. Do not sit all the way up, instead "crunch" your abs together then release.
- Reach for the Sky: Start with hands and arms reaching up toward the ceiling. Then, use your upper abs to lift your shoulders upwards then release for one rep.
- Clappers: Start with arms extended horizontally. Then use your mid-abs to crunch and lift back off the ball, bringing your hands together in a clap for one rep.

Core Back — Back Extension

- Lay face down on the back extension bench, connecting your feet behind the foot braces. Your upper body should be past the end of the bench so you can bend at the waist, allowing for your head to nearly reach the ground. Using your back muscles, lift yourself up into a prone position for one rep. Keep your hands behind your head. If you feel unusual pain, discontinue this exercise.

Cardio — 15–30 minutes (walk at fast pace, or bike)

- This is not a leisure stroll. Instead walk briskly with long strides. You may opt to use intervals of increased elevation, as if you're walking uphill. If on the bike, choose a route that includes some hills to climb. You may also choose to increase walking or biking speeds with intervals of slower paces.

DAY 2 — Legs and Biceps

AT HOME

Squats

- Start standing upright with feet shoulder-width apart or slightly wider. Keep your chest perpendicular to the ground as you bend at the knees, not at the hip. Lift your arms forward to provide a counter weight. You might start with your back to a wall so you can focus on activating the legs. Squat down until your legs create a 90-degree angle or less, then stand up pressing from the heels for one rep.

Forward Lunges

- Start standing upright. Take a large stride forward, lowering yourself until your front leg and back leg are both at nearly a 90-degree angle. Then push into your front heel and foot to raise back up to a standing position for one rep. Switch legs.

Plank — 6 sets, 30 seconds each, /plank

- Use the push-up position (or from forearms) and hold for 30 seconds. Then rest for 10 seconds. Keep back straight, with shoulders locked, engage core, and keep head up.

Cardio — 15–30 minutes (walk at fast pace, or bike)

- This is not a leisure stroll. Instead walk briskly with long strides.

You may opt to use intervals of increased elevation, as if you're walking uphill. If on the bike, choose a route that includes some hills to climb. You may also choose to increase walking or biking speeds with intervals of slower paces.

AT GYM

Dumbbell Squats

- Use two dumbbells of equal weight holding one in each hand. Start standing upright with feet shoulder-width apart or slightly wider. Keep your chest perpendicular to the ground as you bend at the knees, not at the hip. Squat down until your legs create a 90-degree angle or less, then stand up pressing from the heels for one rep.

Dumbbell Curls

- Stand holding a dumbbell in each hand with your arms hanging by your sides. Ensure your elbows are close to your torso and your palms facing forward. Keeping your upper arms stationary, exhale as you curl the weights up to shoulder level while contracting your biceps.

Leg Press

- As machines differ, the general guidelines include: adjust the machine so you can get a 90-degree angle in the legs, and avoid going too far into the stretch.

Bicep Machine

- As machines differ, the general guidelines include: adjust the machine so you do not overextend the elbow, and so you can pull the curl all the way into your chest.

Core: Ab Ball series — Starting position is the same for each of the following exercises, with your lower back on the Ab Ball so your rear-end is barely touching.

- Crunch: With arms crossed in front of your chests, contract your lower and mid-abs to raise your shoulders and upper back off the ball for one rep. Do not sit all the way up, instead "crunch" your abs together then release.
- Reach for the Sky: Start with hands and arms reaching up toward the ceiling. Then, use your upper abs to lift your shoulders upwards then release for one rep.
- Clappers: Start with arms extended horizontally. Then use your mid-abs to crunch and lift back off the ball, bringing your hands together in a clap for one rep.

Core Back — Back Extension

- Lay face down on the back extension bench, connecting your feet behind the foot braces. Your upper body should be past the end of the bench so you can bend at the waist, allowing for your head to nearly reach the ground. Using your back muscles, lift yourself up into a prone position for one rep. Keep your hands behind your head. If you feel unusual pain, discontinue this exercise.

Cardio — 15–30 minutes (walk at fast pace, or bike)

- This is not a leisure stroll. Instead walk briskly with long strides.

You may opt to use intervals of increased elevation, as if you're walking uphill. If on the bike, choose a route that includes some hills to climb. You may also choose to increase walking or biking speeds with intervals of slower paces.

DAY 3 — Shoulders

AT HOME

Lateral Raise

- Stand or sit with a dumbbell in each hand at your sides. Keep your back straight, brace your core, and then slowly lift the weights out to the side until your arms are parallel with the floor, with the elbow slightly bent. Then lower them back down slowly.

Overhead Press

- Stand or sit and bring a weighted bar or dumbbell to chest level located in front of your shoulders, gripping with your palms facing forward. Press up without any assistance from the lower body.

Reverse Shoulder Flies

- Stand with feet shoulder-width apart, holding dumbbells at your sides. Bend at the hips, bringing your chest forward and almost parallel to the floor. Allow the weights to hang straight down (palms facing each other) while maintaining a tight core, straight back, and slight knee bend. Raise both arms out to your side, on an exhale. Keep a soft bend in your elbows. Squeeze the shoulder blades together as you pull them toward the spine. Lower the weight back to the start position as you inhale.

Plank (from push-up position or on forearms) — for 6 sets, 30 seconds each

- Use the push-up position (or from forearms) and hold for 30 seconds. Then rest for 10 seconds. Keep back straight with shoulders locked.

Cardio — 15–30 minutes (walk at fast pace, or bike)

- This is not a leisure stroll. Instead walk briskly with long strides. You may opt to use intervals of increased elevation, as if you're walking uphill. If on the bike, choose a route that includes some hills to climb. You may also choose to increase walking or biking speeds with intervals of slower paces.

AT GYM

Front Dumbbell Raise

- Stand with your feet about shoulder-width apart. Let your arms hang in front of you with the dumbbells in front of the thighs (palms facing the thighs). Your back is straight, your feet are planted flat on the floor, and your abdominal muscles are engaged. Lift the weights upward while inhaling. Your arms are extended, palms facing down, with a slight bend in the elbows to reduce the stress on the joints. Pause briefly when your arms are horizontal to the floor. Lower the dumbbells to the starting position (at the thighs) with a slow and controlled motion while exhaling.

Side Dumbbell Raises

- Stand or sit with a dumbbell in each hand at your sides. Keep your back straight, brace your core, and then slowly lift the weights out to the side until your arms are parallel with the floor, with the elbow slightly bent. Then lower them back down slowly.

Shoulder Press

- Stand or sit and bring a weighted bar or dumbbell to chest level located in front of your shoulders, gripping with your palms facing forward. Press up without any assistance from the lower body.

Reverse Shoulder Flies

- Stand with feet shoulder-width apart, holding dumbbells at your sides. Bend at the hips, bringing your chest forward and almost parallel to the floor. Allow the weights to hang straight down (palms facing each other) while maintaining a tight core, straight back, and slight knee bend. Raise both arms out to your side, on an exhale. Keep a soft bend in your elbows. Squeeze the shoulder blades together as you pull them toward the spine. Lower the weight back to the start position as you inhale.

Cardio — 15–30 minutes (walk at fast pace, or bike)

- This is not a leisure stroll. Instead walk briskly with long strides.

You may opt to use intervals of increased elevation, as if you're walking uphill. If on the bike, choose a route that includes some hills to climb. You may also choose to increase walking or biking speeds with intervals of slower paces.

DAY 4 — Back and Triceps

AT HOME

Lawnmowers

- Start in a split stance (left foot forward for right hand dumbbell, right foot forward for left dumbbell), and bend at the hip. With the dumbbell in your right hand, pull back as if starting a string-pull lawnmower. Repeat with the left hand.

Tricep Kickbacks

- Start in a split stance (left foot forward for right hand dumbbell, right foot forward for left dumbbell), and bend at the hip 45 degrees. Hold dumbbells in each hand and bring upper arms in parallel with your upper body, which should create a natural bend at the elbow. The "kickback" is extending the elbow backward to straighten your arms.

Reverse Flies

- Stand with feet shoulder-width apart, holding dumbbells at your sides. Bend at the hips, bringing your chest forward and almost parallel to the floor. Allow the weights to hang straight down (palms facing each other) while maintaining a tight core, straight back, and slight knee bend. Raise both arms out to your side, on an exhale. Keep a soft bend in your elbows. Squeeze the shoulder blades together as you pull them toward the spine. Lower the weight back to the start position as you inhale.

Superman

- Lie on the ground, face down with your arms and legs extended. Keeping your arms and legs straight (but not locked) and your torso stationary, simultaneously lift your arms and legs up toward the ceiling trying to form an elongated "U" shape with your body. As your back arches, your arms and legs lift several inches off the floor. Hold for two to five seconds and lower back down to complete one rep.

Ab Crunch — 3 sets, 30 reps

- Lie down on your back. Plant your feet on the floor, hip-width apart. Bend your knees and place your arms across your chest (or hold your hands behind your head). Crunch your abs by lifting your upper body until your shoulders and back lift off the ground slightly.

Alternating Leg Raise — 3 sets, 30 seconds

- Start by lying on your back on an exercise mat, face up with your legs straight. Place your arms by your sides with your palms facing down or place your hands under your glutes. Engage your core as you lift your legs 3–5 inches off the ground. Keep your legs straight and off the ground, and bring one leg up slowly, then lower it while avoiding it resting on the ground. Switch legs.

Cardio — 15–30 minutes (walk at fast pace, or bike)

- This is not a leisure stroll. Instead walk briskly with long strides. You may opt to use intervals of increased elevation, as if you're walking uphill. If on the bike, choose a route that includes some hills to climb. You may also choose to increase walking or biking speeds with intervals of slower paces.

AT GYM

Lawnmowers

- Start in a split stance (left foot forward for right hand dumbbell, right foot forward for left dumbbell), and bend at the hip. With the dumbbell in your right hand, pull back as if starting a string-pull lawnmower.

Tricep Kickback

- Start in a split stance (left foot forward for right hand dumbbell, right foot forward for left dumbbell), and bend at the hip 45 degrees. Hold dumbbells in each hand and bring upper arms in parallel with your upper body, which should create a natural bend at the elbow. The "kickback" is extending the elbow backward to straighten your arms.

Wide Grip Cable Pull Downs

- Reach up and grab the bar with each hand. Your thumbs should be pointing toward each other, and your grip should be wider than your body so your arms and torso form a 'Y.' Look straight ahead and pull the weight down until the bar nearly touches your chest.

Close Grip Cable Rows

- Grip a narrow handle, seated on a bench in an upright position with legs slightly bent. Pull the handle towards your abdomen by using your back muscles. Slowly return to the starting position by extending your arms.

Tricep Machine

- Adjust the arm levers so you can get a full extension. After selecting the weight, push the levers away from your shoulder until they are fully extended. Focus on using the tricep muscles only.

Core: Ab Ball series — Starting position is the same for each of the following exercises, with your lower back on the Ab Ball so your rear-end is barely touching.

- Crunch: With arms crossed in front of your chests, contract your lower and mid-abs to raise your shoulders and upper back off the ball for one rep. Do not sit all the way up, instead "crunch" your abs together then release.
- Reach for the Sky: Start with hands and arms reaching up toward the ceiling. Then, use your upper abs to lift your shoulders upwards then release for one rep.

- Clappers: Start with arms extended horizontally. Then use your mid-abs to crunch and lift back off the ball, bringing your hands together in a clap for one rep.

Core Back — Back Extension

- Lay face down on the back extension bench, connecting your feet behind the foot braces. Your upper body should be past the end of the bench so you can bend at the waist, allowing for your head to nearly reach the ground. Using your back muscles, lift yourself up into a prone position for one rep. Keep your hands behind your head. If you feel unusual pain, discontinue this exercise.

Cardio — 15–30 minutes (walk at fast pace, or bike)

- This is not a leisure stroll. Instead walk briskly with long strides. You may opt to use intervals of increased elevation, as if you're walking uphill. If on the bike, choose a route that includes some hills to climb. You may also choose to increase walking or biking speeds with intervals of slower paces.

DAY 5 — Wildcard

You choose exercises from the previous days to target the legs, chest, biceps, shoulders and core. Include cardio of your choice as well.

For week number 2, you can repeat this schedule but add weight/time to the exercises if possible. Or you may want to join a gym, consult a trainer, or become a member at my virtual gym ansonbwalker.com for weekly plans, exercise guidance, meal plans and much more!

Defeating Myths about The Walker Lifestyle

Myth #1. Working out with weights will make me "bulky."

I hear this a lot from women. They fear they are going to look like a female Russian shot putter. But you know what? It's physically impossible for a woman to look like a man because God made women as women, and men as men. Unless they're injecting horse steroids, it's impossible for a woman to look masculine because she is feminine. The only thing they're gonna do is add lean, petite, sexy muscle to their frame that they've got already. That's it. In all my twenty years of training people, I don't have one girl or woman who looks masculine.

Besides, it's also impossible to get "bulky" after lifting weights a few times. It takes a few months to develop the kind of lean muscle I'm talking about. But in the end, women who have trained with me always appreciate their new look. Weight training only enhances what they've got that much more. Everybody wants a shapely booty, but you don't get that booty by sitting on the couch or even from running on the treadmill for hours on end. You've got to work from that squat rack, leg press, and lunges. That's how you get a booty.

Unfortunately for women, and it's not fair, it takes women longer than men to transform their body fat into muscle. They don't have testosterone. It's a little harder for them too because they have more body fat than men. For example, after childbirth, new mothers have a body that has been devoted to feeding their baby, storing fat and hormones to keep their baby healthy. It's rough on them, to say the least. But I'm telling you, the ones I've trained come back for six to eight weeks of training and BAM. They can have that fit body they want.

Myth #2. Exercise always makes me feel "sore." (aka, No pain, no gain.)

I know many of you cringe when you hear, "No pain, no gain." Here's the truth: It doesn't have to be that way. You don't have to, nor should you, experience pain from exercise. Here's how.

First off, you don't go into the gym on day one, especially after a layoff of several months or years, and try to rebuild Rome. That's only going to prevent you from being able to walk the next day.

Instead, you've got to knock a little dust off the muscles with some light weights and high reps during the first week or so, which wake the muscles up. You should feel them talking to you saying, "Here we are." And that's good, because it means they are responding. But you shouldn't feel sore. Take baby steps that first week to two weeks and focus on technique. Don't be a knucklehead by pushing heavy weights. Let's live to see day two. Let's live to see day three. In three to four weeks, you can take it up a notch. The following month, you can take it up another notch. In six months, we are rebuilding Rome.

Remember, you're competing against yourself. Forget about Brutus over there benching 400 lbs. You're not competing with Brutus. You're competing with you. The weights are irrelevant. The fact that you're in there and just moving some weight is what's relevant. That's what's important.

Now, you can do yourself a few favors. For example, drink down an isolate protein shake with 30 grams of protein within 30 minutes of your workout. Also, give the muscle groups that you trained some extra movement. If you did chest and triceps, then choose some cardio that integrates your upper body, like an elliptical with arm motion. That helps work the lactic acid, which causes soreness, out of the muscles. You can also take it a step further. When you get in the shower that night, use the warmth of the water to help stretch those areas. Then turn the water temperature to as cold as you can stand it, which also helps reduce the lactic acid.

Soreness also results from dehydration. So drink water with bio-chain amino acids (BCAA) that I told you about. Plain water doesn't have these electrolytes, salt, potassium, B12, and B3 to help your muscles repair after being worked out. I'm also not opposed to taking a pain-reliever like ibuprofen. It's not something you should need to take daily, but if the pain gets to be too much, then you can afford a few every now and then.

Myth #3. Eating healthy is too expensive.

This one is really a no-brainer. Eating unhealthy food is actually more expensive. You can't afford to eat unhealthy food because five or ten years from now, when you've got diabetes, you're gonna wish you had eaten healthy. Eating unhealthy is only setting yourself up for visits to the doctor's office with high blood pressure, heart conditions, all the stuff that goes along with foods with empty calories, too much sugar, lack of nutrition, fried foods, and over-the-top portions of carbs. But if you stick with my 80–20 rule, you can afford a "cheat meal" every once in a while. Over time, you'll have less desire for them anyway. They won't be worth the food coma or hangover feeling you get.

Besides, you don't have to buy both unhealthy foods *and* healthy varieties. And you can learn to eat healthy in affordable ways. For example, on Saturdays or Sundays I like to cook in bulk for the week whether I'm grilling chicken, venison, or something else. That brings my meal cost down to under $5.

Changing the way you eat is definitely a lifestyle choice, but it doesn't have to cost you an arm and a leg. You just learn to buy the good stuff and avoid the bad, so the bill should be about the same. Then, if you're smart, you can plan ahead and buy — and cook — in bulk, which saves money too.

Myth #4. Cardio is the best way to lose weight.

I disagree with this 100 percent. Cardio does help the heart and cardiovascular system, and it does burn calories to help lose weight. But it doesn't do it as well as strength training. First, we need to use weight training to prevent having brittle bones, especially for women. The older we get, the more concerned we need to be with bone density, and resistance training is the way to support healthy bones. Second, weight training burns more calories than cardio. After lifting weights, the body continues to burn more calories for up to ten hours. You don't get that from cardio. A few minutes after finishing with cardio, your heart rate returns to normal. So when you're done with cardio, you're done burning calories.

It's not even close when it comes to deciding whether to do cardio or weights. If I had to pick, I would take the weights every time. But the great news is we don't have to pick. We live in America. We live in a First World country where we can do both. If you combine cardio with weights, you're gonna win and you're gonna win big. Plus, working out with weights will help your body shape. If you only do cardio, you risk looking like a super-skinny marathon runner. I don't believe that's what people want. Instead, we can develop lean muscle that has some shapely and healthy curves.

Besides, it's not even healthy to do long-distance running or biking. The wear and tear really adds up, and over time it will break you down. If all you do is extreme amounts of cardio, you won't make it to sixty-five years old without hip replacements, hurting back, hip and knee replacements. I will say that doing cardio is better than doing nothing. But you need to know it's not the best way to lose weight.

Myth #5. Counting calories is the best way to monitor your diet.

Some people are wired to count calories, measure portions, and weigh all their foods. It can help you discover the nutritional values and caloric costs with foods. So it's not all that bad, and to lose weight you have to burn more calories than you eat. But I like to simplify things and use common sense. For example, you only need to eat one plate of food. If you follow my ground rules for nutrition, you don't need to worry about counting calories. I'd rather you focus on the quality of what you're eating instead of counting calories.

I like to say, "Your belt doesn't lie." What I mean is, instead of counting calories, if you notice your belt is a little tighter and you need to loosen it a notch, then you know you have to get in the gym and pick up your intensity a little bit.

Still, if you're eating clean 80 percent of the time, eating lean and green with the less legs the better, then counting calories isn't really an issue. See chapter 6 for further details.

Myth #6. Yoga will take care of my fitness goals.

I had to do yoga to develop an appreciation for yoga. And I've got mad respect for people who do yoga. It's hard, and what yoga does better than anything is it gives you flexibility and strength for better balance. But yoga does not build lean muscle mass or help your cardiovascular health. You will still need to weight train and do cardio on top of yoga to get the best results. I encourage people to do yoga, because I've tried it and I know it's hard. But it's not the only thing you will need to improve your health, nor will it help the way you look.

Myth #7. CrossFit is the latest and greatest way to get fit.

I know this about CrossFit: orthopedic surgeons love people who do it. There are hundreds of ways to exercise, and CrossFit is one of them that combines Olympic Lifts with gymnastics in a group setting with daily competitions. If it works for you, and you're using the proper technique, congratulations. But if you're over thirty-five years old and competing against others in their twenties with reps, speed, and weight, you're going to compromise your form and increase your risk of injury. It's just human nature. You're fixing to hurt yourself doing high-impact lifts like overhead squats, bear crawls, jerks, and snatches, as well as box jumps and handstands. It's just a matter of time before you tear up your wrists, shoulders, and knees. That's why orthopedic surgeons love them.

Don't get me wrong, I have mad respect for the elite, national CrossFit competitors because they put themselves through a ton of work. But for most people, there's just no need to do all those movements. It's just a good way to get hurt. Plus, that style of exercise does not flatter the female body. Ever seen a beautiful, shapely Olympic weightlifter? That's because there's a reward for adding strength and, therefore, bigger muscles.

So I caution you about drinking the CrossFit Kool-Aid. If there's one thing I like about it, it's the group classes, which builds community and a sense of accountability. But you can find that at a gym.

Myth #8. A healthy lifestyle and daily exercise takes too much time.

This one is a challenge for ALL of us. But the answer is simple: Get up early. If you are serious about this, you'll make time. You'll set the alarm. You'll go to bed earlier. For those who say, "Anson, I've never been able to get up early," I call your bluff. Because I know if you have to be on a plane at 6:00 a.m. for a vacation, you'll be sure to make it on time. Why? It's important to you. It's the same with exercise. If it's important — like one of your top five priorities — you'll find a way to get to the gym or do the work at home.

Besides, you can get a great workout in 30–40 minutes. So a "lack of time" is not a valid reason. It's an excuse. My bootcamps take 45 minutes of weight training and core work. Then they do 15–30 minutes of cardio on their own.

You may need to get your workout in before the kids wake up, or during your lunch hour, or after work. But it's not only possible, it's a *lifestyle decision*. You have to create the time, make an appointment on your calendar for your wellbeing. That's what I do. I schedule it. It works for me. And I know you can do it too. I train doctors, lawyers, engineers, teachers, grandmothers, grandfathers, mothers, fathers, sisters, brothers, uncles, and they all make the time. So I know if you want it, you'll do it.

Once you get in a groove, you'll actually feel like something's missing on the days you don't work out. Your mind and body feed off the new energy, increased blood flow, and endorphins. If you do this for ninety days, you're not going back. What I've seen over the course of my lifetime is there is a ninety-day barrier. Make it to ninety days and you'll be in at 100 percent. If not, you won't.

Remember, there are seven days in the week. I'm just asking for about one hour for five of those days. That's just five hours of the 168 hours available in one week that you have to transform your life. That's possible. With The Walker Lifestyle mindset, it's even likely. You can make a choice right now to change your life for the better. I know you can do it, and I will be right there encouraging you and cheering you on to success.

About the Author

Anson overcame tremendous odds to lead thousands of people to reach their fitness potentials. A certified personal trainer and wellness consultant with more than 25- years experience, Anson is also a highly decorated veteran with the U.S. Navy, and mentor with Wounded Warriors. A popular radio show host on ESPN's *The Zone*, Anson is often called to provide motivational talks, sharing his comeback story after serving time in jail, multiple injuries, and a near-death accident. A former investment advisor, Anson earned an MBA from Delta State University, is certified by the American Sport and Fitness Association and the American Fitness Professional Association. He has been awarded the National Defense Service Medal, Global War on Terrorism Medal, Good Conduct Medal, and Sharp-Shooting Ribbon. Based in Madison, Mississippi, Anson is engaged to Tiffany Gunn.

Connect with Anson at:

Facebook — https://www.facebook.com/anson.b.walker
LinkedIn — https://www.linkedin.com/in/ansonwalker/
Instagram — https://www.instagram.com/abwalker7/?hl=en
AnsonBWalker.com
Email: anson@ansonwalker.com

You can connect with me on:

- http://www.ansonbwalker.com
- https://www.facebook.com/anson.b.walker
- https://www.linkedin.com/in/ansonwalker
- https://www.instagram.com/abwalker7/?hl=en

Subscribe to my newsletter:

- http://www.ansonbwalker.com

Rabbi Zalman Schachter-Shalomi: A Life of Renewal

INTRODUCTION

According to legend (Babylonian Talmud, Gittin 6b), after the destruction of the second Temple, Rabbi Yohanan ben Zakkai led a small group of Jewish refugees to the town of Yavneh, where they set about rebuilding Judaism for the new realities they faced. Beginning in the mid-1960s, Rabbi Zalman Schachter (better known as Reb Zalman, a less formal title he preferred)[1] argued that it was time for Yavneh II, a deep rethinking of how to be (or do) Jewish today. Indeed, he believed that all religious traditions were in urgent need of updating in the face of dramatic shifts in world events, technology, and consciousness. As he saw it, there was no aspect of human life that was unaffected by such events as the Holocaust; Hiroshima and Nagasaki; the Civil Rights, Hippie, and Feminist Movements; and the moon landing. In light of these phenomena, it was humanity's task to consciously build a new world with a renewed understanding of the interconnection and interdependence of all being. This, he insisted, required bold religious and cultural adaptation.

---

1. He would add the name Shalomi (from *shalom*, peace) later in life to balance his family name, Schachter, which means kosher slaughterer in Yiddish, the family occupation for several generations. The name change was suggested to him by his Sufi friend and colleague, Pir Vilayat Inayat Khan. See *My Life in Jewish Renewal: A Memoir*, 182. The term *Reb* means Mr. or Sir in Yiddish (as opposed to rabbi or professor).

Because of his commitment to these views and his experimental nature, Reb Zalman was often a controversial figure in his lifetime, beloved by many and dismissed or reviled by others. His students and admirers saw him as a kind and accessible mentor, a creative interpreter of Kabbalah[2] and Hasidism,[3] and a visionary religious innovator. Those who opposed him felt that he had betrayed the values and standards of traditional *Yiddishkeit* (Jewish life) and was too easily influenced by shifting intellectual and cultural trends. However, this opposition diminished significantly in his later years, as many former skeptics and opponents came to appreciate his creativity, learnedness, and demonstrated effectiveness. As he aged, Reb Zalman also honed and steadied his approach to renewal, consolidating various of his experiments and working with colleagues and students to establish the Jewish Renewal Movement and related professional training programs. As part of his *harvest* process, he also (re)produced an array of writings, videos, and audio recordings, sharing his erudition and passion for the tradition, while continuing to call for thoughtful innovation. By the turn of the century, Reb Zalman was increasingly viewed as a significant bridge figure between Eastern European Hasidism and North American Jewish life—a Neo-Hasidic[4] sage and spiritual innovator. Today, Jews the world over wear the B'nai Or rainbow *tallit* (prayer shawl) he

---

2. Literally "that which has been received," this Hebrew term is used to refer to the Jewish mystical tradition as a whole and more technically to the flowering of Jewish mystical activity in medieval Western Europe (beginning c.1150). See Daniel C. Matt, *The Essential Kabbalah: The Heart of Jewish Mysticism* (San Francisco: HarperCollins, 1995).

3. *Hasidism* (from the Hebrew root word *hesed*, loving-kindness) is a term used for various Jewish pietistic groups throughout Jewish history. In this context, it refers to the Eastern European mystical revival movement that emerged in the late eighteenth-century and continues to flourish today. See *Hasidism: A New History*, edited by David Biale et al. (Princeton, NJ: Princeton University Press, 2018).

4. This term refers to twentieth and twenty-first century Jewish figures who draw on Hasidic teaching and tradition for religious and/or cultural inspiration but who are not part of a traditional Hasidic community. See